BIOLOGY OF CELLS AND ORGANISMS

Laboratory Manual

F A L L   2 0 1 3

Michael Muller

Department of Biological Sciences
University of Illinois at Chicago

Hayden-McNeil Sustainability

Hayden-McNeil's standard paper stock uses a minimum of 30% post-consumer waste. We offer higher % options by request, including a 100% recycled stock. Additionally, Hayden-McNeil Custom Digital provides authors with the opportunity to convert print products to a digital format. Hayden-McNeil is part of a larger sustainability initiative through Macmillan Higher Ed. Visit http://sustainability.macmillan.com to learn more.

Printed in the United States of America

10 9 8 7 6 5 4 3 2 1

ISBN 978-0-7380-6276-1

Hayden-McNeil Publishing
14903 Pilot Drive
Plymouth, MI 48170
www.hmpublishing.com

Muller 6276-1 F13

TABLE OF CONTENTS

SAFETY IN THE LABORATORY

While it is important to learn and have fun in the laboratory, safety should always be your number one goal. Throughout this lab manual, safety recommendations and precautions are given, but there is no substitute for common sense. Handling equipment and hazardous chemicals always involves some risk. However, by being cautious and using your head, you can avoid almost all of this risk.

The first laboratory, your Teaching Assistant (TA) will go over the following points with you. If you miss the first lab, be sure to go over these points with your TA:

- Location of the following:
  - Fire extinguishers
  - First aid kit
  - Emergency exit routes
  - Telephone
  - Bathroom

- If you are pregnant or have a medical condition that interferes with your safety (such as a weak immune system, seizures, blackouts, etc.), please inform your TA and your professor. This information will remain private, but it will ensure that if a situation does arise, appropriate measures can be taken.

- If you have any concerns about the chemicals used in laboratory, ask to see the Material Safety Data Sheets (MSDS). These can also be obtained on the internet at the following URL: http://www.ehs.cornell.edu/msds/msds.cfm.

General Safety Procedures for All Laboratories

- No food or drink in laboratory. Smoking is not permitted in the building.

- Wear appropriate clothing in laboratory. Loose clothing and dangling jewelry may get caught on equipment. Always wear shoes in laboratory.

- Always report chemical spills to your instructor. They will direct the appropriate cleanup.

- Report suspected equipment failures to your instructor.

- Never mouth pipette!

- Never leave an open flame unregulated.

- Be careful with hot or sharp equipment. Your mother told you not to run with scissors for a reason.

- Wear safety goggles when working with concentrated acids, bases, caustic materials, and organic solvents. Always pour chemicals slowly.

- If you have an open wound, make sure it is protected with a waterproof bandage.

- Tell your instructor if you have any safety concerns in laboratory. This may include both the equipment, the materials used, or the behavior of other students. If you have concerns about your TA, please inform the professor.

- Always wash your hands after laboratory. Wash hands *before* going to the bathroom if you must go during laboratory. Wash hands before touching eyes, mouth, or other mucous membranes.

- Leave equipment and materials in your laboratory station neatly organized for the next group. Report any broken or missing equipment to your teaching assistant.

QUANTITATIVE TECHNIQUES AND ERROR IN MEASUREMENT

CHAPTER 1

After completing this laboratory, you should be able to:

- Define what is meant by error in measurement and identify sources of error in experimental procedures.

- Obtain skills in the use of pipettes, rulers, and spectrophotometers.

- Perform statistics designed to quantify error in measurement.

- Prepare a computer-generated standard curve and use the equation of the standard curve to determine the concentration of an unknown solution.

Part 1—Ruler Technique and Approximation in Measurement

One common misconception both in science and in life is that all measurements are accurate. This is simply not true; any measurement made with a measuring device is approximate. If you measure the same object two different times, the two measurements may or may not be the same. The difference between two measurements is called a **variation** or an **error** in the measurements. In this case, however, "error" does not mean mistake. Since you can never know the "true" measurement of an object, you have no real way to determine which of two measurements is the most accurate. The "error" is just a mathematical means to show the degree of uncertainty in a measurement.

Error in measurement may be represented by a **tolerance interval**. To determine the tolerance interval in a measurement made with analog equipment (i.e., thermometer, pipette, ruler, etc.), add and subtract one-half of the precision of the measuring instrument to the measurement, rounding up if necessary. For example, your 5.0 ml pipette has a precision of 0.1 ml. This is the smallest interval of measurement marked on the pipette. The tolerance interval is therefore ± 0.05 ml. Even though the smallest marked interval is 0.1 ml, you can make a good estimate as to where your volume is between these two intervals. So, if you took a measurement and determined it to be 3.32 ml, the measurement, including the tolerance interval, is 3.32 ± 0.05 ml.

Error in measurement may also be expressed by a percentage of error. For example, a measurement of 9.00 meters may be said to be off by 2%. This means that the actual measurement could be between:

9.00 − (2% of 9.00) and 9.00 + (2% of 9.00)
9.00 − (0.02 * 9.00) and 9.00 + (0.02 * 9.00)
9.00 − 0.18 and 9.00 + 0.18
8.82 to 9.18 meters

Error in measurement may also be indicated by the terms "rounded" or "to the nearest" when a high degree of accuracy is not essential. When dealing with rounded measurements, remember the basic rules for rounding: 0–4 rounds down and 5–9 rounds up. For example, the length of a side of a square to the nearest centimeter is 10 cm. This means that the actual length of the side could be between 9.5 cm and 10.4 cm (since all of these values round to 10).

Measure the below lines in millimeters. You should be able to measure them up to 0.1 mm.

A _____

B _____

C _____

D _____

Record the measurement of each below:

A _____ B _____ C _____ D _____
Compare your data to those of your classmates. Are your measurements identical?

Part 2—Pipette Technique and Experimental Uncertainty

Your instructor will demonstrate the use of the pipettes in measuring fluid volumes. To measure the desired amount, immerse the pipette in the appropriate fluid and draw it up beyond the desired volume using a suction device. Notice how the fluid will adhere to the edges of the pipette, but bow down in the middle. This is the **meniscus**, the concave upper surface of a column of water caused by surface tension. Hold the pipette vertically and allow the fluid to slowly escape until the bottom of the meniscus touches the desired volume. To best measure volumes, you need to get down at eye level and make sure the bottom of the meniscus is at the desired volume (Figure 1.1). Any drops hanging from the tip of the pipette should be removed by touching the tip to the inside of the beaker from which the solution was drawn.

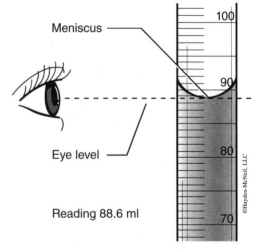

Figure 1.1. Proper Pipette Reading Technique

To practice your pipetting technique, your group should obtain a 5 ml graduated serological pipette and two plastic beakers. Fill one of the plastic beakers with about 200 ml of tap water (note the graduations along the side of the plastic beaker). Record the mass of the second, empty beaker to the nearest tenth of a gram using one of the balances found on the middle lab bench. Be sure you remember which of the balances you used to make your measurement and use this balance for the remainder of the laboratory. Now use the pipette to add the following volumes of water in milliliters to the empty beaker:

5.00	4.20	3.20	2.60
4.80	4.00	3.10	1.20
4.30	3.80	2.90	0.90

A total of 40.00 ml should have been added to the empty beaker.

Now we are going to test your accuracy using a much more precise technique. Refill your first cup with water if necessary, dry out the cup used previously and weigh it again. Now use a 25 ml pipette and pipette two aliquots of 20.00 ml into the empty beaker. Just like before, a total of 40.00 ml should have been added to the beaker. We will now analyze the class data for both of these exercises to determine their accuracy.

VERIFYING TECHNIQUES

To check the accuracy of your pipetting, weigh the amount of water added to the beaker and use the density of water to convert this mass to a volume. The density of water at room temperature in laboratory is 0.998 g/ml. If you remember from the metric system lab, the density of water at sea level is 1.00 g/ml. However, since we are not at sea level, the gravitational attraction of the earth is slightly less (0.2% less) so we will account for this.

Weigh the beaker containing the 40 ml of water and record the mass below. Subtract the mass of the empty beaker from the filled beaker to obtain the actual mass of the water in the beaker. This operation, subtracting the mass of the container from the mass of the material plus the mass of the container is called **taring**.

Mass of beaker containing water:

12-Step: __52.8__ g   2-Step: __58.9__ g

Minus mass of empty beaker:

12-Step: __16.6__ g   2-Step: __16.6__ g

Equals the mass of the water:

12-Step: __36.2__ g   2-Step: __42.3__ g

Have other members of your lab perform this experiment using the same pipette, beakers, and balance. Be sure that you carefully dry the empty beaker so that there will be no error from water still remaining in the beaker. Record all data on the blackboard or other location indicated by your laboratory instructor.

Your measurement (12-Step)

__36.2__ g __36.3 27__ ml

Your measurement (2-Step)

__42.3__ g __42.38__ ml

Are the class values all equal? Do any equal 40.00 ml? Why or why not?

Calculate the experimental error of your measurements as a percentage by using the following equation:

$$\% \text{ error} = \frac{\text{measured value} - \text{theoretical value}}{\text{theoretical value}} \times 100$$

$$= \frac{\text{your value } H_2O - 40.00}{40.00} \times 100$$

% error (12-Step) = __0.095 -9.5%__

% error (2-Step) = __5.75%__

Did your % error increase or decrease when you measured out two 20.00 ml solutions instead of the twelve-step measurement sequence? Defend your answer.

ERROR IN MEASUREMENT

Record the total volumes on the blackboard. All of your classmates will do the same, so you should have a large data set. Record the class data in Data Tables 1.1 and 1.2, found at the end of this laboratory. Different students probably obtained slightly different values for their measurements. Even if gross errors (such as incorrect calculations, failure to follow directions, or incorrect readings) are ruled out, there would still be some variation due to minor experimental and chance errors. Therefore, the measurements you have made are not true values but are simply estimations of a true value. Some estimations obtained by the class are lower than the true value, while others are higher. When it is important for scientists to obtain the best estimation of the true measurement, they repeat the measurement several times and calculate a **mean** value. A mean value can be calculated by taking the sum of all of the data points and dividing it by the number of data points measured.

$$\text{Mean} = \frac{\Sigma \, (\text{measurements})}{N}$$

where N is the number of measurements taken and the Greek letter Σ, sigma, means "sum of" (so Σ (measurements) means "sum of the measurements").

However, a mean by itself often does not convey enough information about the data set. Often, scientists need to know the amount of variation or "scatter" of the data points around the mean. One method of generating this is to calculate **standard deviation** of the data. This estimator of error is usually expressed as a mean plus or minus the value of the standard deviation.

Variance and standard deviation are calculated as follows:

$$\text{variance} = \frac{\Sigma \, (\text{measured value for each sample} - \text{mean})^2}{N-1}$$

standard deviation = square root of variance

Standard deviation is commonly calculated because it gives statistical parameters of how closely your data is to the mean. The range of the mean ± 1 standard deviation will include approximately 67% of the data. The range of the mean ± 2 standard deviations will include approximately 95% of the data. If the standard deviation is small, the data lie very close to the mean, but if the standard deviation is large, the data are dispersed widely from the mean.

Part 3—Use of the Beer-Lambert Law to Generate a Standard Curve Used in the Determination of an Unknown

Many organic molecules absorb light. Our ability to see color at all is due to the presence of pigment molecules in our eyes that are sensitive to certain wavelengths of light. If an object appears to be blue, it is because it contains molecules that absorb red, yellow, and green particles of light called **photons**, while the blue photons are reflected back to our eyes. A **spectrophotometer** is a device used to measure the amount of light absorbed by a solution (Figure 1.2). A spectrophotometer contains a special **light source**, a **prism**, an **aperture slit**, and a **light meter** (Figure 1.3). The light source shines white light, a combination of all visible light waves, into the prism. The prism separates the light into many colors. The prism is adjustable, so that only a narrow range of wavelengths will shine on the aperture slit. The slit is thin, so only one wavelength will shine through onto the sample you wish to measure. Some of the light will be **absorbed** by the solution, while the rest is **transmitted** through. The light meter measures the amount of light transmitted through and calculates the light absorbed.

Figure 1.2. A Digital Spectrophotometer

Oftentimes the chemical we wish to measure is mixed with a solution of other chemicals. These chemicals also have absorbant properties and when we measure absorbance, we will want to find a way to remove or subtract the absorbances of these additional chemicals. This can be accomplished by preparing a **blank**. A blank is a solution that contains all of the chemicals in our experimental solution *except* the chemical we are interested in. For example, if we have a solution of BSA in a 0.5 M NaCl solution, the blank will be a 0.5 M solution of NaCl. To calibrate the spectrophotometer, we first measure the absorbance of the blank. The computer inside will note the amount of absorbance and transmittance in the blank and set this to be the 100% Transmittance / 0 Absorbance point. (Basically it is like the taring process we discussed earlier.) When we measure the experimental tube, any additional absorbance must be due to the presence of our chemical since we have already taken into account the absorbance of the other chemicals in the solution.

So, why do we care about the amount of light absorbed by a solution? The amount of light absorbed by a solution is proportional to the concentration of the solution. This relationship is known as the **Beer-Lambert Law**. If one has a solution of unknown concentration, a **standard curve** can be generated to determine this relationship. A scientist will prepare several solutions of known concentrations, measure the absorbance of each, and then graph this relationship. A best-fit straight line is then generated and the equation of the line determined. Now all one has to do is measure the absorbance of the unknown solution, substitute this absorbance into

the equation of the line (the y-value) and solve for the concentration (the x-value).

The Beer-Lambert Law holds true for any wavelength of visible light. However, to improve accuracy, you will first need to find the wavelength of light that is maximally absorbed by your solution. This wavelength is known as the **absorbance maximum** or the **λ_{max}**. The Greek letter λ, lambda, is the variable used to denote wavelength of light. To determine λ_{max}, one measures the absorbance of light at several wavelengths and plots the result, generating a bell-shaped curve known as an **absorption spectrum**. The peak of an absorption spectrum is the λ_{max}. By setting the spectrophotometer to the λ_{max} when generating a standard curve, you can be assured that any subtle changes in concentration will be measured accurately. Measurements made at λ_{max} are more precise than measurements made at other wavelengths.

In this experiment, you will be given a solution of a dye, **bromophenol blue**, of an unknown concentration. You will also be given a stock solution of bromophenol blue at a known concentration (0.030 mM). Use this stock solution first to generate an absorption spectrum for bromophenol blue. From this, you will calculate λ_{max} of bromophenol blue. You will then prepare a series of dilutions of known concentration, measure their absorbance, and generate a standard curve. Finally, you will measure the absorbance of the unknown and use the standard curve to calculate the concentration of the unknown solution.

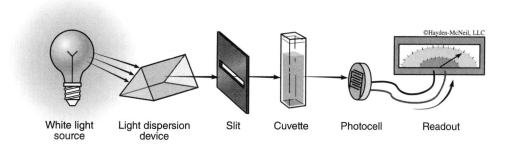

©Hayden-McNeil, LLC

White light source · Light dispersion device · Slit · Cuvette · Photocell · Readout

Figure 1.3. Internal Components of a Spectrophotometer

USE OF THE SPECTROPHOTOMETER—GENERATION OF AN ABSORBANCE SPECTRUM FOR BROMOPHENOL BLUE

For this experiment, you will be using a digital spectrophotometer (Figure 1.2). Digital spectrophotometers are very accurate and simple to use. Use the directions below to generate the absorption spectrum of bromophenol blue.

1. Prepare two solutions, one containing 8.0 ml of distilled water (the blank) and one containing 8.0 ml of 0.030 mM bromophenol blue (the experimental solution).

2. Set the spectrophotometer to 400 nm by adjusting the nm up and nm down buttons.

3. Carefully wipe off the cuvette containing the blank. You want to wipe off the cuvette to remove any excess water and fingerprints as these can distort your measurements and damage the spectrophotometer.

4. Lift the sample door and insert the cuvette with the blank into the cuvette holder.

5. Carefully shut the sample door and press the "0 Abs / 100% Transmittance" button. The screen should say "Setting Blank" and then display 0.000 A.

6. Remove the blank. Wipe off the experimental cuvette and insert in the cuvette holder. Carefully shut the sample door. The absorbance reading will be displayed on the screen.

7. Record the absorbance reading in Data Table 1.3 (found at the end of the laboratory) and remove the experimental cuvette.

8. Adjust the wavelength of light to the new setting, and repeat the above instructions.

9. When you have completed Data Table 1.3, you will need to prepare a graph of the absorption spectrum. See Appendix A for assistance on how graphs are to be prepared in this course.

You must *always* reblank the spectrophotometer when you change wavelengths. The chemicals in the blank may have different absorbant properties at the new wavelength that need to be taken into account.

GENERATION OF A STANDARD CURVE FOR BROMOPHENOL BLUE AND DETERMINATION OF THE CONCENTRATION OF AN UNKNOWN

To generate a standard curve, you will need to prepare a **dilution series**, a series of solutions of known concentration. Use Table 1.1 to prepare a dilution series.

To calculate the concentration of each dilution, use the following formula:

$$C_1 V_1 = C_2 V_2$$

where:

C_1 = concentration of stock solution
V_1 = volume of stock solution used to prepare dilution
C_2 = concentration of dilution
V_2 = final volume of dilution

For example, the concentration of the first dilution is as follows:

$$C_1 = 0.030 \text{ mM} \quad V_1 = 1.0 \text{ ml} \quad V_2 = 8.0 \text{ ml}$$

$$\begin{aligned} C_2 &= C_1 V_1 / V_2 \\ &= (0.030) * (1.0) / (8.0) \\ &= 0.0375 \text{ mM} \end{aligned}$$

Repeat the above calculations for the remaining dilutions. Record your calculations in Data Table 1.4. For the purpose of this lab, relax the restriction on significant figures (i.e., write out 0.0375 mM and do not round to 0.038 mM).

MICROSCOPY AND MEASUREMENT

CHAPTER 2

After completing this exercise, you should be able to:

- Learn the use of the metric system, the meaning of prefixes, and how metric units are interrelated.

- Perform calculations using scientific notation.

- Define and distinguish between magnification and resolution.

- Calculate total magnification of objects viewed with a compound light microscope.

- Identify the parts of the compound light microscope.

- Define field of view and depth of field and understand how increasing magnification affects these properties.

- Properly obtain a microscope from the storage cabinet and set it up at your workstation.

- Prepare a wet mount and view it under various magnifications.

- Discuss the differences between a compound light microscope and a dissecting scope.

- Discuss the differences between Transmission Electron Microscopy (TEM) and scanning electron microscopy (SEM).

The elements of microscopy have been known and used for hundreds of years. This simple invention has proven to be invaluable in the study of biology as it enables us to see organisms and objects that are far too small to be seen by the naked eye. The human eye can distinguish objects that are about 0.2 mm in size—a typical cell is 0.02 mm in diameter—10× smaller than can be seen with the unaided eye! Imagine the surprise of early biologists when they used a microscope to examine a typical drop of pond water. They could not believe that a seemingly sterile drop of water contained hundreds of single-celled organisms!

A microscope functions by using a series of lenses to **magnify**, or increase in size, the image. However, the quality of a microscope is not based solely upon its ability to simply magnify images but also on its ability to resolve them. **Resolution** is the ability to distinguish two points located close together as separate points. Without adequate resolution, magnification is useless. You can better understand the relationship between magnification and resolution by looking at an analogy based upon internet web browsing. Imagine you go to a website with several thumbnail pictures of your classmates that say "click here to enlarge." When you click on one image, a new, much larger (magnified) image appears. If the picture of your classmate has high resolution when magnified, you will be able to see much detail in the magnified picture. If the picture of your classmate has low resolution when it is magnified, it will look all blocky because the details were lost when the low resolution image was generated.

Parts of the Compound Light Microscope

THE LENS SYSTEM

The microscope you will be using most in laboratory is called the **compound light microscope** (Figure 2.1). It is called a compound microscope because the light is magnified twice, first by the **objective lens** and again by the **ocular lens**. The objective lens is the lens that is closest to the slide and is frequently attached to a rotating **nosepiece** so that you may easily change magnifications without altering the position of your slide. The ocular lens

is the lens that you look through. The ocular lenses of your microscope magnify light ten times; this is written as a 10× lens. If you only have one ocular lens, then your microscope is a **monocular** microscope. If your microscope has two ocular lenses, then your microscope is a **binocular** microscope. Most binocular microscopes contain a mechanism to move the two lenses closer together or farther apart to match the views **interpupillary distance** (the distance between the user's pupils). Doing so allows you to look through each lens and reduce eyestrain over prolonged use.

The objective lenses are a series of lenses located on a rotating nosepiece. The rotating nosepiece has a textured ring that allows you to grip and move the lenses without physically touching the sensitive objectives. When you rotate the objectives, you should feel them click into place as the lens becomes engaged. This is known as the **working position**. Your microscope has three objectives, the lowest powered is known as the scanning objective, and it magnifies light 4×. The middle-powered lens is a 10× lens and the high-powered lens is a 40× lens (Figure 2.2). Total magnification can be easily calculated by taking the magnification of the objective lens and multiplying it by the magnification of the ocular lens.

THE STAGE

The slide rests upon the **stage** and is held in place by the **stage clip**. The stage clip rests on the side of the slide—it does *not* get placed on top of the slide as doing so will bend the stage clip. To properly place the slide on the stage, simply use the lever to pull the stage clip aside, place the slide on the stage so that the corner sits in the **slide rest** and gently move the stage clip back so that it rests on the side of the slide. There is a hole in the center of the stage to allow light to pass through the slide. The slide may be moved back and forth and up and down by turning the **stage adjustment knobs**.

THE LIGHT SOURCE

The light source must be turned on by plugging in the microscope and flipping the power switch to on. Light intensity may be adjusted three ways.

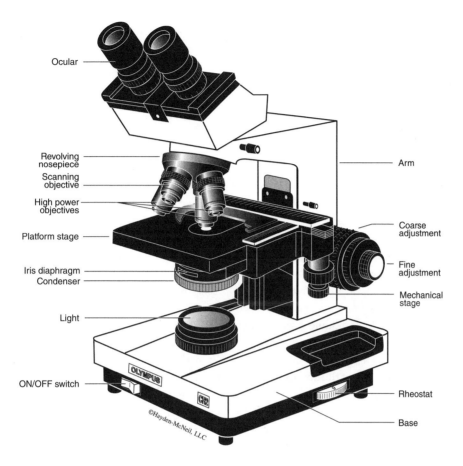

Figure 2.1. The Compound Light Microscope

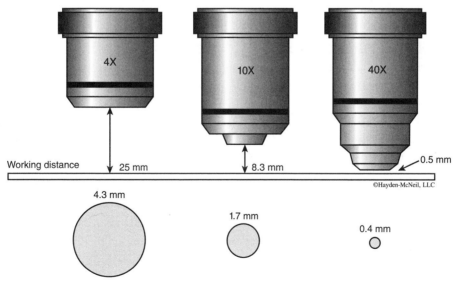

Figure 2.2. Objective Lens Properties

There is a **dimmer dial** located directly below the power switch. Turning this will increase or decrease the brightness of the lamp. The **condenser lens** is used to focus the light from the lamp. Opening or closing the **iris diaphragm** can also be used to further control the amount of light passing through the slide.

THE FOCUS KNOBS

Once the scanning objective is set and the slide is centered on the stage, you may look through the ocular lenses to view the image. If the image is blurry, turn the large **coarse focus** knob to focus the image. You may notice that the microscope focuses the image by moving the stage up and down. *Always use the scanning objective lens to initially focus the image.* The scanning objective is shorter and you do not run the risk of the objective lens colliding with the slide, which can ruin your slide and scratch the objective lens! Once the image is more or less in focus, you can tweak the focus by turning the **fine focus** knob.

The microscopes we are using in lab are **parfocal** microscopes. An image focus using the scanning objective lens should be in focus when higher powered objectives are engaged. Some minor adjustments may be needed with the fine focus, however, if the microscope is not perfectly calibrated. You should *never* adjust the coarse focus when using any objective other than the scanning objective.

Care and Use of the Microscope

When working with a microscope, you should always observe the following rules:

- Carry the microscope with two hands. Always hold the microscope by the arm with one hand and place your other hand under the base. *Do not grab or hold the microscope by the stage!*

- The microscopes are heavy and some may be located high on cabinet shelf. If you do not feel that you are tall enough to safely remove or return the microscope to the top shelf, ask your TA or another student for assistance.

- Keep all parts of the microscope dry. If the image appears cloudy, it is probably dirty. You may clean the lenses by using lens-cleaning fluid and lens paper or cloth. Never use Kimwipes or paper towels to clean the lens as these may lead to scratches on the lens.

- When you are done using the microscope, remove the slide and return the scanning objective to the working position.

Microscope Activities

The activities below are designed to teach you some of the properties of the compound light microscope as well as give you practice in its use. You may do these in any order.

THE LETTER "e" AND PREPARATION OF A WET MOUNT

Prepare a wet mount of the letter "e" (or any letter that looks different upside down) by first cutting the letter out of a newspaper. Take a slide and place a drop of water in its center. Use tweezers to place the letter e on the drop right-side up. Place one edge of the coverslip on the slide near the drop and gently lower it onto the slide. This forces air out the edge and prevents air bubbles from forming (Figure 2.3). Place the slide so that the letter "e" is right-side up as you are looking directly at it on the stage. Now turn on the microscope and focus on the letter "e." What do you observe about the orientation of the letter "e"?

Take your eyes away from the ocular lens and look directly at the stage. Turn the stage adjustment knob so that the slide moves toward the left. Recenter the slide and turn the knob the same direction again. Which way did the image move? As light moves up the microscope, the lens systems invert the image so that up is down and right is left. This is why the letter "e" looks upside down and why when you move the slide to the left, it appears as if it is moving toward the right when observed through the ocular lenses.

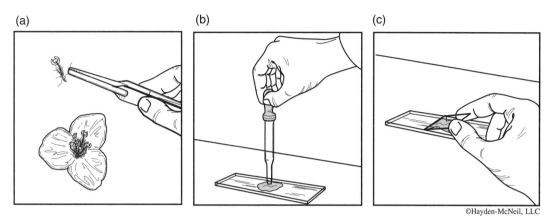

Figure 2.3. Preparation of a Wet Mount

Now turn the objective from the scanning lens to the 10× lens. Notice how the amount of the image you can see is reduced. The amount of the slide visible at each magnification is known as the field of view. The diameter of the **field of view** for each lens is given in Figure 2.2.

You should also notice that the **brightness** of the light is reduced when you increase magnification. This is due to the reduction of the field of view. As the field of view decreases, the number of photons entering your eyes also decreases, making the light look dimmer. As you increase magnification, you may need to adjust light levels to compensate for this.

CROSSED THREADS AND FOCAL PLANE

Prepare a wet mount of two different-colored crossed threads. Observe these under the scanning objective and notice how much of each thread is in focus. Now increase magnification and observe how the amount of the threads you can hold in focus has decreased. The thickness of a specimen that can be seen in focus at a given magnification is known as the **focal plane** (in some literature, the focal plane is called **depth of field** or **depth of focus**). At the highest magnification, the focal plane is typically smaller than the diameter of a cell, so that only the top portion or the bottom portion may be viewed with clarity. This can often reduce the resolution of your microscope, making it difficult to clearly see cellular details at high magnification.

WET MOUNT OF POND WATER

Prepare a wet mount of pond water. Observe the many single-celled animals and plants living in the pond water. How many different forms do you see? Try to use the stage adjustment knobs to follow a swimming organism around, keeping in mind that the apparent direction of movement is reversed by the lens systems of the compound light microscope.

Stereoscopic Microscope

The **stereoscopic microscope** (Figure 2.4) is fundamentally different from the compound light microscope. With a compound light microscope, there is only one objective lens in use. If you are using a binocular compound light microscope, there is an optical device inside that splits the light and creates two identical images, one for each ocular. These images then pass through your eye lens system and are projected onto your retina. Your brain receives signals from your left and right optic nerve and superimposes these images. Since they are identical, your brain interprets this as being flat and you see a two-dimensional image. The stereoscopic microscope, however, has two independent lens systems, each offset a few degrees from vertical. Because of this, the image that is projected onto your right retina is different from the image projected onto your left retina. When your brain superimposes these two different images, the differences between the two are interpreted as depth and you see a three-dimensional image.

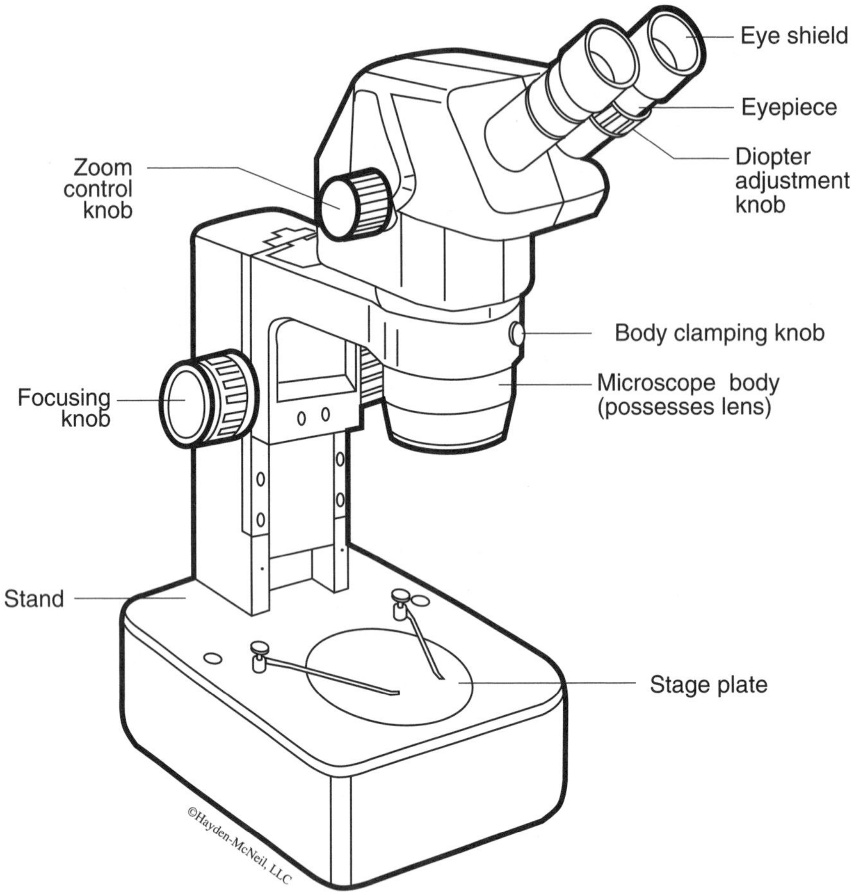

Zoom control knob

Focusing knob

Stand

Eye shield

Eyepiece

Diopter adjustment knob

Body clamping knob

Microscope body (possesses lens)

Stage plate

©Hayden-McNeil, LLC

Figure 2.4. Parts of a Stereoscopic (Dissecting) Microscope

Stereoscopic microscopes are commonly called **dissecting scopes** and are used when manipulating (as opposed to just viewing) larger objects. Magnification is frequently $2\times$ up to $20\times$. What you sacrifice in magnifying power, however, you make up in functionality. As the name implies, these scopes are frequently used in dissection, where the three dimensional viewing properties will be more useful than high levels of magnification. There is ample space between the stage and the objectives so that you can manipulate objects with probes and tweezers.

Transmission Electron Microscopy

There is a limit to the amount of magnification possible when using visible light as an illumination source. The wavelengths of visible light are between 450 and 650 nm and when trying to magnify beyond $1000\times$, interference patterns become pronounced and you cannot resolve the image. For magnifications above $1000\times$, a different illumination source must be used.

A **transmission electron microscope (TEM)** is used when magnifications between $1000\times$ up to $20,000\times$ are needed. The TEM is essentially a vertical television tube with an electron gun at the top and a screen at the bottom. Electrons are accelerated by the electron gun, pass through the tube, and strike the screen, which creates a glow. To view a sample, it must first be coated with a reflective metal (such as gold) and then placed in the stream of the electrons. Where the electrons strike the specimen, they will be reflected and will appear on the screen as shadows. The overall image of the specimen on the screen is a series of light areas and shadows. The screen image can then be printed out. This is known as a transmission electron micrograph. TEM is used when you wish to view the details of cellular structures such as the folding of Golgi bodies (Figure 2.5).

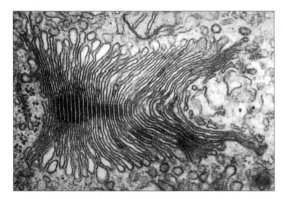

Figure 2.5. TEM Micrograph of the Golgi Apparatus

A sample that is to be viewed with a TEM must be carefully prepared. Through a process known as **fixing**, the sample is imbedded in a rigid epoxy plastic and impregnated with metal salts. The epoxy plastic is then very thinly sliced. This process obviously kills the tissue.

Scanning Electron Microscopy

A **scanning electron microscope (SEM)** is to TEM what a dissecting microscope is to a compound light microscope. A compound light microscope has one lens system and produces a highly magnified, two-dimensional image while a dissecting microscope has two offset independent lens systems and produces a lower magnification, three-dimensional image. Likewise, a TEM produces a highly magnified, two-dimensional image while a SEM produces a lower magnification, three-dimensional image. Two offset electron guns are used. A computer acts like your brain and superimposes these images creating a single, three-dimensional image. SEM are used when you wish to view larger, three-dimensional structures like the hairs on a fly's head or the highly sculpted outer wall of a pollen grain (Figure 2.6).

Figure 2.6. SEM Micrograph of Pollen Grains

The Metric System

The metric system was developed in France during the 1790s by the offices of Napoleon as a means to standardize the many confusing nationalistic systems of measurements. Previous systems were very complicated to use because there was no standard hierarchy for measurements. You simply had to memorize that there were 12 inches in a foot, three feet in a yard, 5280 feet in a mile, etc. (even older systems were based upon the body measurements of the king, which would change as one king died and someone else was crowned). The metric system is based upon powers of ten. There is a system of prefixes that denote how many powers of ten above or below the base unit a particular measurement is. The metric system is used in almost all countries in the world (the U.S., of course, being a notable exception).

We will be looking at four types of measurements using the metric system: length, volume, weight, and temperature. The base unit of length is the meter. It was defined as being one millionth of the distance from the North Pole to the equator (through Paris, of course). The standard unit of volume is a liter (l) and it is defined as the volume of one square decimeter at sea level (more on the prefixes below). The standard unit of weight is the gram. It was defined as the weight of a cubic centimeter of pure water at sea level. A commonly used way of remembering the interrelationships of length, weight, and volume in the metric system is $1 \text{ cm}^3 = 1 \text{ ml} = 1 \text{ g}$. The temperature scale is known as Celsius or Centigrade (°C) and it is based upon dividing the separation of the freezing point of water (0°C) and the boiling point of water (100°C) into 100 equal units.

Let's now take a few minutes and speak of the useful set of "prefixes" used in the metric system sometimes referred to as the System Internationale (SI). One of the mathematical advantages of the metric system is its combination of metric terminology with its decimal organization. There are several prefixes that are associated with a decimal position and can be attached to the base metric unit in order to create a new metric unit. The knowledge of the decimal meaning of the prefix establishes the relationship between the newly created unit and the base unit.

For example: the prefix "centi" means 10^{-2} or 1/100 so if I take a hypothetical base unit like the "zot" and I attach the centi- prefix in front, I create a new unit called the "centizot" and we immediately know that this new unit is 1/100th of a zot. A listing of the commonly used prefixes is given below in Table 2.1.

Standard Conversions

1 cm³ of water = 1 g = 1 ml

Scientific Notation

As you can see, some of the prefixes refer to very large or very small numbers. Writing out these large or small numbers can be quite cumbersome. No one wants to have to read or write 98700000000000 or 0.00000000000456. Scientific notation is a system that has been developed to easily write these numbers. In scientific notation, a number has a coefficient and an exponent (power) of ten. To convert a number to scientific notation, follow the steps below:

1. To find the coefficient, take the number, drop the non-significant zeros, and put a decimal point after the first digit.

2. To find the exponent, count the number of places from the decimal to the end of the number. For numbers smaller than one, do not count the zero before the decimal point because it is only a place holder.

In our example above, 98700000000000, the coefficient is 9.87 and the exponent is 10^{13} making the number 9.87×10^{13}. For 0.00000000000456, the coefficient is 4.56 and the exponent is 10^{-12}, making the number 4.56×10^{-12}.

Table 2.1. Prefixes Used in the Metric System

Prefix	Symbol	Decimal Equivalent	Exponential Equivalent
Nano-	n-	0.000000001	10^{-9}
Micro-	μ- or u-	0.000001	10^{-6}
Milli-	m-	0.001	10^{-3}
Centi-	c-	0.01	10^{-2}
Deci-	d-	0.1	10^{-1}
	base unit	1	10^{0}
Deca- (Deka-)	da-	10	10^{1}
Hecto-	h-	100	10^{2}
Kilo-	k-	1000	10^{3}
Mega-	M-	1,000,000	10^{6}
Giga-	G-	1,000,000,000	10^{9}

Multiplication and Division of Numbers Written in Scientific Notation

Multiplication of numbers written in scientific notation is easy. All you have to do is multiply the coefficients, add the exponents, and then possibly adjust the coefficient and exponents so that they are written properly.

For example:

1.0×10^2 * 1.0×10^5 becomes
$(1.0 * 1.0) \times 10 (2 + 5) = 1.0 \times 10^7$

3.1×10^2 * 6.9×10^5 becomes
$(3.1 * 6.9) \times 10 (2 + 5) = 21.39 \times 10^7 = 2.139 \times 10^8$

Notice that since you converted 21.39 to 2.139 by moving the decimal point to the left, you had to add one to the exponent (you reduced the coefficient by a factor of 10, so you must increase the exponent by one factor of ten to keep everything equal).

Division is the same as multiplication, except that you divide the coefficients and then subtract the exponents. For example:

1.0×10^2 / 1.0×10^5 becomes
$(1.0 / 1.0) \times 10 (2-5) = 1.0 \times 10^{-3}$.

3.1×10^2 / 6.2×10^5 becomes
$(3.1 / 6.2) \times 10 (2-5) = 0.50 \times 10^{-3} = 5.0 \times 10^{-4}$

Notice that since you converted 0.50 to 5.0 by moving the decimal point to the right, you had to subtract one from the exponent (you increased the coefficient by a factor of 10, so you must decrease the exponent by one factor of ten to keep everything equal).

CELLULAR STRUCTURE AND FUNCTION

CHAPTER 3

After completing this laboratory, you should be able to:

- Describe features that are common to all cells.

- Identify the defining characteristics of prokaryotic and eukaryotic cells, and be able to compare and contrast the two cell types.

- Identify and describe the major cellular components of prokaryotic and eukaryotic cells.

- Differentiate between plant and animal cells from living material, prepared slides, as well as from descriptions.

- Discuss the evolutionary significance of increasing complexity from prokaryotic to eukaryotic cells and from unicellular to multicellular organisms.

In biology, there is a progression of order. Starting with the smallest and progressing toward the largest, we have the following:

- Atoms
- Molecules
- Macromolecules and Polymers
- Cells
- Tissues
- Organs
- Organ Systems
- Organisms
- Populations
- Communities
- Ecosystems

In this course, we will be focusing primarily on Molecules to Organisms. In future courses, you will study higher interactions of organisms in populations, communities, and ecosystems.

In 1665, **Robert Hooke** first used the word "**cell**" to refer to the basic unit of life. Hooke had made a preparation of a piece of cork and, when viewed under a microscope, he was able to "...perceive it to be all perforated and porous, much like honeycomb. These pores of cells were not very deep, but consisted of a great many little boxes."

One hundred and seventy-three years later, two German biologists, **Matthias Jakob Schleiden** and **Theodor Schwann**, published what is called the **cell theory**. The essence of cell theory states that *the cell is the basic unit of life and all living organisms are composed of one or more cells or the products of cells.*

Biologists recognize three organizational plans for cells. **Prokaryotic cells** lack a nuclear envelope, chromosomal proteins, and membranous cytoplasmic organelles. Bacteria and blue-green algae are prokaryotic cells. **Eukaryotic cells** possess the structural features the prokaryotes lack. Protozoan, fungal, plant, and animal cells are eukaryotic. A recently defined third group of cells, the **archaeans**, were originally thought to be prokaryotic, but detailed analysis of their ribosomes and genetic organization indicated that they were actually more closely related to eukaryotic cells. Today, they are only found in extreme environments, such as salt flats and thermal vents. As they are rare in nature, we will not be observing them in laboratory, but be aware that they do exist and understanding archaeans is important in understanding the evolution of life on earth.

Although these three types of cells are distinctly different, they share all of the following characteristics:

- All cells contain a plasma membrane that surrounds a cell and regulates the passage of materials into and out of the cell.

- All cells contain cytoplasm.

- All cells contain enzymes to regulate cellular reactions.

- All cells utilize DNA as the molecule of heredity.

- All cells contain ribosomes for use in the synthesis of proteins.

Prokaryotic Cells

Prokaryotic cells were the first cells to evolve 3.8 billion years ago. Some of the prokaryotic cells alive today have changed little since that time while others have changed dramatically during that time. Heterotrophic prokaryotic cells (cells that cannot produce their own food and must eat to survive) are commonly called **bacteria**.

CHARACTERISTICS OF PROKARYOTIC CELLS

Prokaryotic cells have very simple morphologies (Figure 3.1). However, don't let this apparent simplicity fool you—most of the diversity of prokaryotes is biochemical, not morphological. All modes of living, **autotrophs**, **heterotrophs**, and **decomposers**, are found among the prokaryotes. We will be looking at some of the chemical differences between different types of prokaryotes when we look at bacteriology and health. However, there are some morphological traits that can be used to distinguish bacteria.

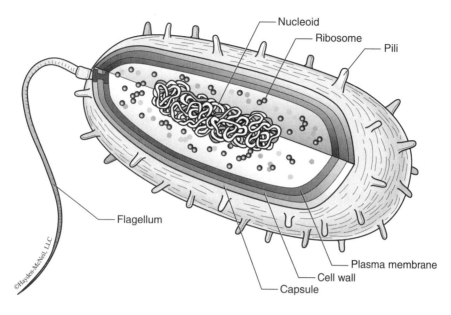

Figure 3.1. Features of a Typical Prokaryotic Cell

There are three general morphologies of bacteria (Figure 3.2). **Cocci** (singular = coccus) are sphere-shaped bacteria, **bacilli** (singular = bacillus) are rod-shaped bacteria, and **spirilla** (singular = spirillus) are comma- or corkscrew-shaped bacteria. Additionally, there are differences in the composition of the bacterial cell walls, which can lead to different staining properties. **Gram-positive** bacteria stain purple under a Gram stain technique while **Gram-negative** bacteria stain pink. All possible combinations of bacterial morphology and Gram-staining properties are known.

The more you study biology, however, the more you will realize that living organisms seem to constantly defy scientists' efforts at classification. Exceptions and intermediate forms will always be found (what do you call a rounded bacteria with two flat ends—is it a short bacillus or a flattened coccus?)

Bacterial Identification

The relative lack of morphological differences in bacteria has lead scientists and doctors to develop a system of biochemical tests to aid in the identification of unknown bacteria. A device known as an Enterotube has been developed to easily perform several biochemical tests on one common family of bacteria that contains many of the frequently encountered pathogenic bacteria (note that in lab, we will be using harmless bacteria). Results from the tests are then quantified and each bacteria is given a numerical code, which can be looked up in a cart, yielding the identity of the bacteria. What used to take several technicians a week can now be done in five minutes!

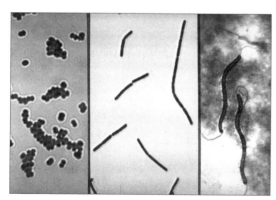

Figure 3.2. Bacterial Morphology: Coccus, Bacillus, Spirillus

PROKARYOTE EXERCISES

- *Bacteria Types Slide*—This slide contains the three bacteria morphologies. Draw the three bacteria morphologies, making sure you indicate the magnification of each. Also, indicate whether the bacteria are Gram positive or Gram negative.

- Your TA will demonstrate the use of an Enterotube. The cultures must incubate for 24 hours. Your Enterotubes will be incubated and returned to you the next week in lab.

Eukaryotic Cells

Eukaryotic cells first appeared over 1 billion years ago (their origin keeps getting pushed back, but they did not become common until 1 billion years ago). This may seem like a long time ago, but eukaryotes are relative newcomers on the earth. Keep in mind that the first prokaryotes appeared over 3.8 billion years ago, so for about 75% of the time that life has existed on earth, it has been strictly prokaryotic.

Eukaryotes are characterized by increased size, complexity, and possible multicellularity. Their cytoplasm contains a nucleus and several membrane-bound **organelles** such as the endoplasmic reticulum, Golgi bodies, mitochondria, peroxisomes, lysosomes, and sometimes chloroplasts and a central vacuole. The evolution of organelles allowed eukaryotes to have a degree of division of labor—each organelle has specialized functions. All of the enzymes and membranes necessary for these functions are contained within the organelle, allowing for an increase in efficiency and a means of protecting the rest of the cell from possibly harmful effects of the enzymes and chemicals contained within. The chart below illustrates some of the basic differences between prokaryotic and eukaryotic cells (Table 3.1).

Eukaryotic organisms include the protists, fungi, plants, and animals. All multicellular organism are eukaryotes. A good rule of thumb: if you can see an organism with the naked eye, it is a eukaryote. In this lab, you will observe a diversity of protist, plant and animal cells.

Protist Cells

Protists are single-celled and colonial eukaryotic organisms. The term "protozoa" means first animal and at one time was used as a phylum name by zoologists. Now it is used as a term of convenience referring to members of the Kingdom Protista. Protozoans are interesting cells to observe because of their unique shapes, modes of locomotion, and often large cytoplasmic organelles.

Prepared slides of various amoebas, flagellates, and ciliates are available in the lab. When observing these slides, be sure you focus on the slide using the **scanning objective (4×)**. From there, you may increase magnification to higher powered objectives. The information on the next pages will help you in your observations and appreciation of protists.

Table 3.1. A Comparison Between Prokaryotic and Eukaroytic Cells

	Prokaryotic Cells	Eukaryotic Cells
Nuclear Material	Single naked DNA loop + plasmids	DNA arranged in many chromosomes
Nucleus	Absent	Present
Organelles	Absent in most	Present
Size	1–10 μm	10–100 μm
Ribosomes	Smaller	Larger
Cell Division	Binary fission	Mitosis
Gene Organization and Expression	Operons	Much more complex organization

Amoeba

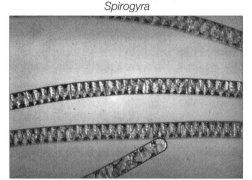

Paramecium

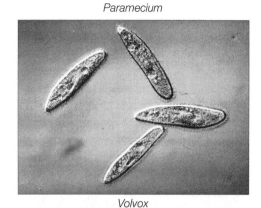

Spirogyra

Volvox

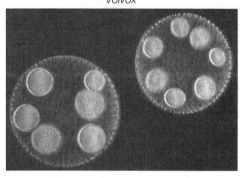

Figure 3.3. Four Protists

AMOEBA

- Member of the Order Sarcodina

- Haploid

- Moves and feeds through the creation of pseudopods. Pseudopods are extensions of the cytoplasm that are supported through rapid development of the cytoskeleton.

- Reproduction is almost exclusively asexual through mitosis.

- *Identify:* Plasma membrane, nucleus, cytoplasm

PARAMECIUM

- Member of the Order Ciliates

- Haploid

- Moves and feeds through coordinated beating of thousands of cilia.

- Reproduction is usually asexual through mitotic divions. However, a form of sexuality does exist through conjugation (swapping of micronuclei). Note that during conjugation, genetic material is exchanged, but no new paramecia are created. This is an example of sexuality without reproduction.

- *Identify:* plasma membrane, nucleus, cytoplasm, cilia

SPIROGYRA

- Member of the Chlorophyta (green algae)

- Haploid

- Chloroplasts contain chlorophyll a and b as primary pigments.

- The photosynthetic storage product is starch. Starch is stored in pyrenoids located on the chloroplasts.

- *Spirogyra* is a colony with a filamentous habit.

- Reproduction is usually asexual through mitosis. However, conjugation can occur when two cells grow together and fuse their nuclei.

- *Identify:* spiral-shaped chloroplasts, pyrenoid, cell wall

VOLVOX
- Member of the Chlorophyta (green algae)

- Haploid

- Chloroplasts contain chlorophyll a and b as primary pigments.

- Storage product = starch

- *Volvox* is a ball-shaped colony. The vegetative cells live on the exterior of the clear ball.

- Reproduction is usually asexual, but some vegetative cells can convert to gametes. The sperm swims to an adjacent colony and fertilizes the eggs.

  - The zygote undergoes meiosis and forms a haploid daughter colony inside.

  - The daughter colony will emerge when the parent colony dies or is ruptured.

- *Identify: Volvox* colonies, daughter colonies, vegetative cells

Multicellular Eukaryotes
Multicellular organisms are composed of many specialized cells. The cells have become specialized to perform a specific function or functions. This division of labor has evolved to make the organism more efficient. By specializing, the cells become better able to perform their specific function. However, they often lose the ability to perform other functions, making them unable to survive independently. It is only by working together that the cells are able to keep the organism (and themselves) alive.

The specialized cells are grouped together to form **tissues** that perform particular functions for the organism. The tissues are frequently organized to form **organs** and organs, in turn, are grouped together to form **organ systems**. In this lab, you will examine several cell types that compose organs of plants and animals.

Plant Cells
Plant cells contain all of the standard identifying features of eukaryotes (plasma membrane, nucleus, organelles, etc., see Figure 3.4). They also possess three unique cellular features—**cell wall**, **chloroplasts**, and large **central vacuole**. The cell wall, like the cell wall of bacteria, is a rigid structure that surrounds the cell and prevents the cell from bursting due to changes in osmotic pressure (see Chapter 6 for more on this). However, unlike bacteria, the plant cell wall is composed of the sugar **cellulose** and often it is additionally fortified with **lignin**. Chloroplasts are organelles that perform photosynthesis. However, not all plant cells contain chloroplasts. Cells that are located underground, such as root tissue, may lack chloroplasts. The central vacuole is a large, membrane-bound sac within the cytoplasm that stores metabolic wastes and is involved in the maintenance of turgor pressure. Animal cells may contain a vacuole, but they are not as large as those found in plant cells nor are they involved in the maintenance of turgor pressure.

To better understand plant cells, you will prepare two wet mounts, one from a red onion outer epidermis and one from the growing leaf tip of the aquatic plant *Elodea*.

EXERCISE—ONION EPIDERMIS PREPARATION
- To prepare a wet mount of red onion epidermis, take a razor blade and carefully make a small cut in a portion of the epidermis.

- Now carefully put the razor blade or your fingernail in the cut and pull up. At first, several cell layers will come up, but as you continue to pull, the sample will become thinner and thinner, eventually becoming one cell layer thick.

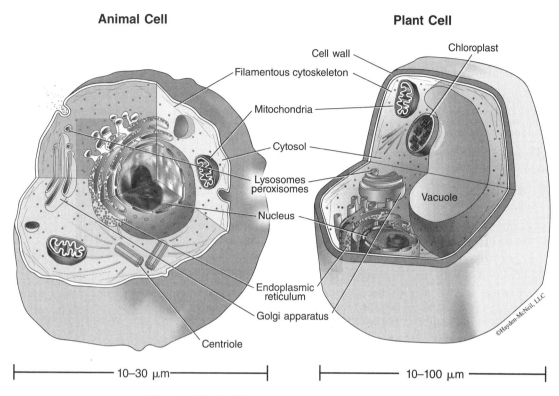

Animal Cell

Plant Cell

Cell wall

Chloroplast

Filamentous cytoskeleton

Mitochondria

Cytosol

Lysosomes peroxisomes

Vacuole

Nucleus

Endoplasmic reticulum

Golgi apparatus

Centriole

©Hayden-McNeil, LLC

├──── 10–30 μm ────┤   ├──── 10–100 μm ────┤

Figure 3.4. Typical Features of an Animal and a Plant Cell

- When the sample finally is removed from the onion, check to make sure that there is a thin section on the tail end of the removed piece. If so, then place the sample on the slide. Place a couple of drops of water on the sample and use tweezers to spread out the sample if necessary.

- Check the sample—if the leading edge is too thick, you may have to use the razor to remove it, leaving behind the thinner tailing edge. When you are satisfied with the sample, place the coverslip and observe.

- Note that you will not need stain as the red pigments in the onion provide a natural stain.

  - Observe the **nucleus** (which is suspended in the central vacuole), **plasma membrane**, and **cell wall**.

  - Why are chloroplasts not present?

EXERCISE—ELODEA *WET MOUNT*

- Remove a growing leaf from the *Elodea* sample provided by your teaching assistant.

- Place the leaf on a slide and prepare a wet mount.

  - Observe the cell wall and chloroplasts.

  - You may see **cytoplasmic streaming** if you leave the sample on the stage for several minutes.

  - Cytoplasmic streaming is the circular movement of the chloroplasts.

  - You see it because the microscope light heats up the cytoplasm, creating a convection current that carries the chloroplasts.

Animal Cells

Animal cells lack a cell wall. As such, they are more vulnerable to osmotic shock. Multicellular organisms, however, usually possess an organ or organ system to maintain proper osmotic balance and prevent body cells from being damaged. What organ prevents this from happening in humans?

EXERCISE—HUMAN CHEEK SCRAPE

- To prepare a cheek cell scrape, use the flat end of a toothpick and lightly scrape the lining of your cheek. Smear the scrapings on a slide.

- Place two drops of water on the scrapings and gently place a coverslip on the sample.

- Add one drop of methyl blue to one edge of the coverslip.

- Take a piece of paper towel or tissue and place it on the coverslip edge opposite to the methyl blue. The water will be absorbed into the paper towel and draw the methyl blue into the sample. This is known as **wicking**.

  - The methyl blue will be drawn into the sample, lightly staining it.

  - If you placed methyl blue directly on the sample, it would be overstained and you would not be able to determine details.

- Observe the **plasma membrane**, **nucleus**, and **cytoplasm**.

Mammalian Histology

You will observe several prepared slides of mammalian tissues. From these, you will see how cell types have become differentiated to perform various functions in our bodies.

NERVOUS TISSUE

Nervous tissue carries electrical impulses from one part of the body to another, providing the body with a rapid means of communication. Most nerve cell bodies reside in the brain or the spinal cord, with the axons and dendrites extending out to interface with muscles or sensory organs.

Obtain a prepared mammalian nervous tissue smear slide. Find a nerve cell and observe the large **cell body** containing the nucleus (Figure 3.5). Extending from the cell body are many cytoplasmic projections. Those that carry electrical impulses toward the cell body are called **dendrites** and those that carry impulses away from the cell body are called **axons**. Note the numerous black dot-like structures at the ends of dendrites and axons. These are the **synapses**, the junctions between one nerve cell and another. At the synapse, the electrical signal is converted to a chemical signal in the form of a **neurotransmitter**. The neurotransmitter is released from the presynaptic terminal, floats across the synaptic cleft, and binds to receptors on the plasma membrane of the postsynaptic terminal. The binding of the neurotransmitter to the postsynaptic terminal can depolarize the plasma membrane of the axon and the electrical impulse will continue.

Table 3.2. Comparison of Animal and Plant Cells

	Plant Cell	Animal Cell
Cell Wall	Present	Absent
Mitochondria	Present	Present
Chloroplasts	Present	Absent
Central Vacuole	Present	Absent
Centrioles during Mitosis	Absent	Present

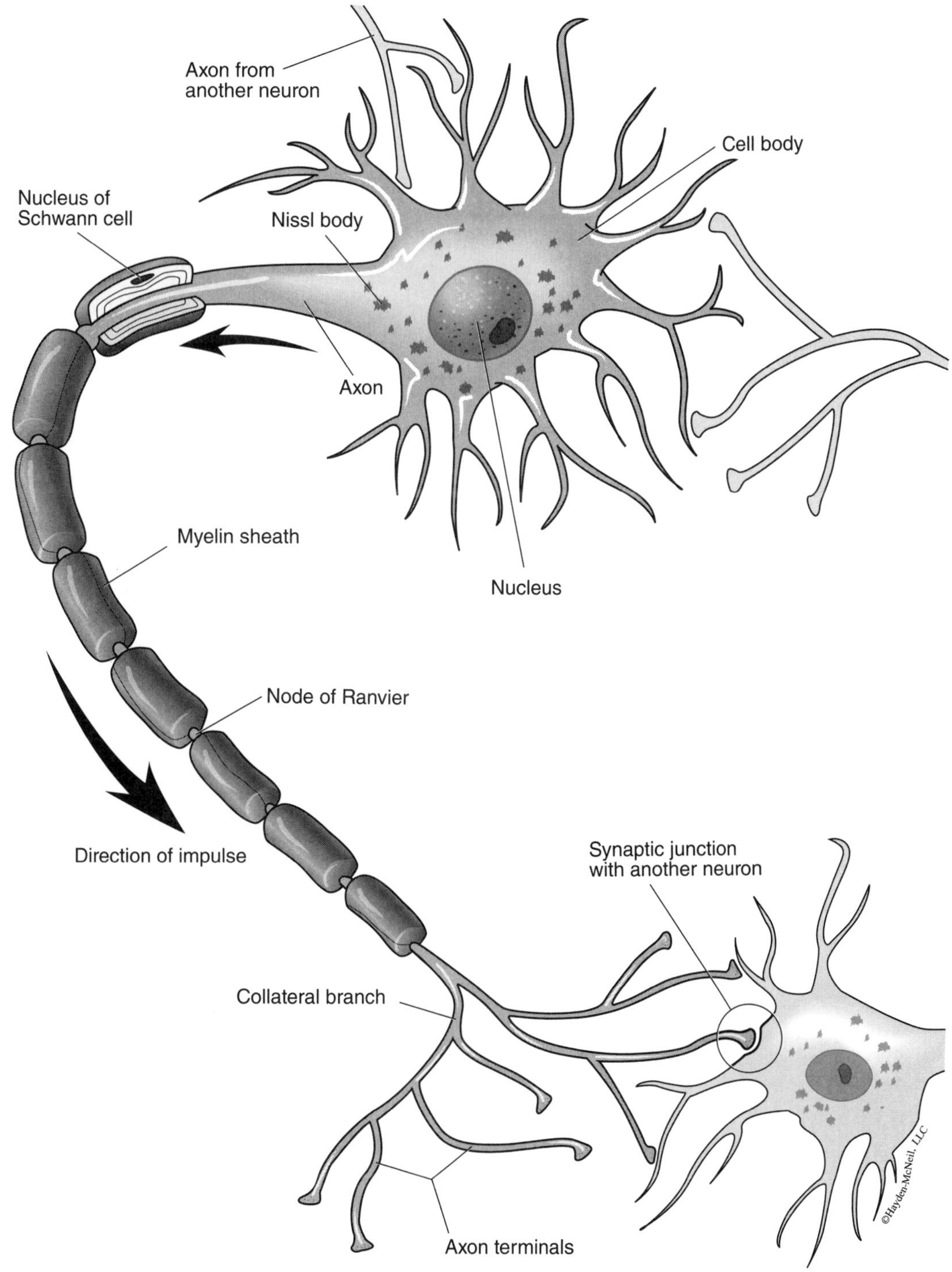

Axon from
another neuron

Cell body

Nucleus of
Schwann cell

Nissl body

Axon

Myelin sheath

Nucleus

35

Node of Ranvier

Direction of impulse

Synaptic junction
with another neuron

Collateral branch

©Hayden-McNeil, LLC

Axon terminals

Figure 3.5. A Typical Motor Neuron

MUSCULAR TISSUE

Muscular tissue is a contractile tissue—it contains mechanisms to alter the length of the tissue. These contractions are generally involved in movement—either locomotion or the movement of something within the organism.

There are three types of muscular tissue found within the human body: **smooth muscle, striated (skeletal) muscle**, and **cardiac muscle** (Figure 3.6). Smooth muscle is an involuntary muscle—contraction and relaxation are not under conscious control. Smooth muscle is found surrounding the digestive tract and under the skin. Smooth muscle derives its name from the lack of striations in the muscle tissue. Striated (skeletal) muscle is a voluntary muscle, under conscious control. When you flex your biceps, you are contracting a skeletal muscle. As the name implies, striated muscle contains striations that demark the **sarcomeres**, the functional unit of a muscle. Cardiac muscle is found only in the heart and also contains striations. Cardiac muscle has internal control of contractions—this is what keeps the heart beating.

CONNECTIVE TISSUES

Connective tissue is characterized by a tissue with **living cells** surrounded by a **non-living matrix** (Figure 3.7). The general term for a living cell in connective tissue is a **fibroblast**. Fibroblasts are typically responsible for the formation of the acellular matrix. Many connective tissues, such as bone and cartilage, are supportive connective tissues. Others, such as blood and loose connective tissue, are not.

CARTILAGE

Observe the cartilage cross section slide. The cartilage will usually lie on the periphery of the sample. Chondrin, the acellular matrix of cartilage, is the homogenous purple structure. Within the chondrin lie several holes, these are the **lacunae**. Within the lacunae lie one to four **chondrocytes**, the cellular component of cartilage (chondrocytes are the fibroblasts in cartilaginous tissue).

Smooth muscle

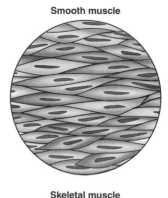

Skeletal muscle

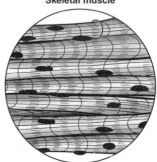

Cardiac muscle

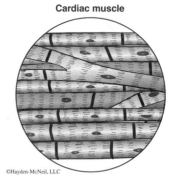

©Hayden-McNeil, LLC

Figure 3.6. Histology of Muscular Tissue

BONE

Observe the bone cross section slide. Because bone is brittle, the cross sections are often thick and opaque, making observations difficult. Bone tissue, unlike cartilage, is a highly vascularized tissue. There are several blood vessels permeating your sample. Your sample will look like several concentric circles compressed together surrounded by dark black dots. Each grouping at a concentric circle is known as a **Haversian system**. At the center of the Haversian system lies the **Haversian canal**, containing a blood vessel. Surrounding the Haversian canal lies the

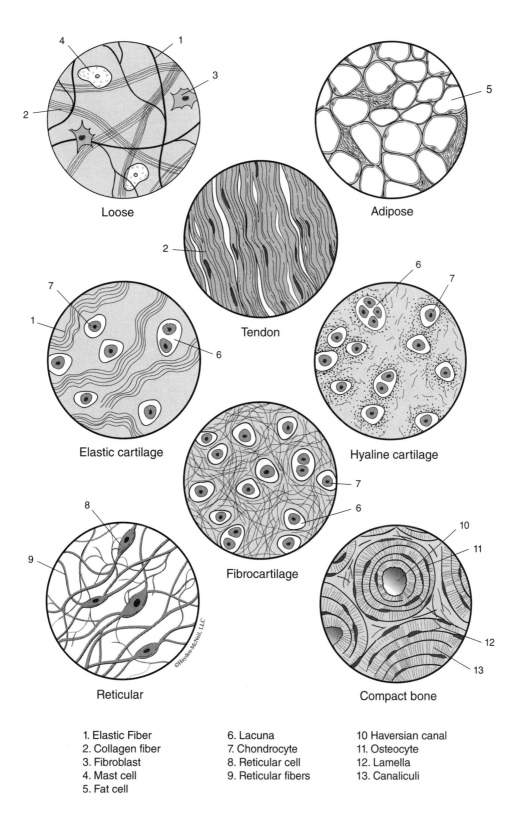

1. Elastic Fiber
2. Collagen fiber
3. Fibroblast
4. Mast cell
5. Fat cell

6. Lacuna
7. Chondrocyte
8. Reticular cell
9. Reticular fibers

10 Haversian canal
11. Osteocyte
12. Lamella
13. Canaliculi

Figure 3.7. Histology of Several Connective Tissues

acellular matrix comprised mostly of the phosphate-rich mineral hydroxyapetite. The living fibroblasts of bone tissue, the **osteocytes**, live in lacunae, which appear as dark spots surrounding the Haversian canal. Lacunae are connected to each other and to the Haversian canal by **canaliculi**, a network of tunnel-like pores that permeates the bone.

Bone is a very dynamic tissue. Haversian systems are constantly being destroyed and reformed. This is because during everyday activities, small microfractures can form in the bone. By themselves, these microfractures do not significantly reduce the strength of the bone. However, over time, they would become larger and seriously reduce the integrity of the bone. By destroying and reforming the Haversian systems, the microfractures are removed and the bone is stronger than before.

BLOOD

Blood does not readily come to mind when one thinks of a connective tissue like bone and cartilage do. This is because blood is not a supportive connective tissue. However, it meets all the criteria of a connective tissue. It has living cells (**erythrocytes and leukocytes**) living in a non-living matrix (**plasma**) (Figure 3.8). Erythrocytes, commonly known as red blood cells, carry blood from the lungs to body tissues. In mammals, erythrocytes lack a nucleus and are produced *en masse* in the bone marrow. Leukocytes, commonly known as white blood cells, are nucleated cells, which function in the immune system, destroying foreign pathogens.

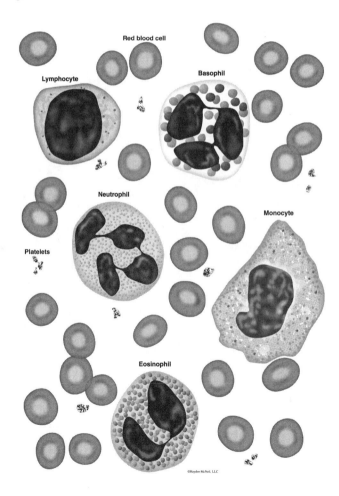

Figure 3.8. Histology of Blood

BIOMOLECULES

CHAPTER 4

After completing this laboratory, you should be able to:

- Know what a polymer is, and which biological molecules are polymers.

- Differentiate between a carbohydrate, a lipid, a protein, and a nucleic acid.

- Identify the monomeric unit of each.

- Understand the principles behind chromatography and calculate an Rf value.

Living systems are composed of millions of different types of molecules, each with their own distinct chemical composition, shape, and function. The vast majority of these molecules can be classified into four major groupings: lipids, proteins, carbohydrates, and nucleic acids. Proteins, carbohydrates, and nucleic acids are all examples of *polymers*—large molecules composed of similar subunits (monomers) covalently bonded together in a long chain. In contrast, lipids, while they can aggregate together as in your cell membranes, do not covalently bond, and therefore are not polymers. The properties of these four important classes of biomolecules are outlined on the following pages.

Carbohydrates

Carbohydrates are the most abundant biomolecule in nature. Carbohydrates are molecules composed of C, H, and O in a ratio of 1:2:1. The monomeric constituent of a carbohydrate is called a *monosaccharide*. The principle functions of carbohydrates include: cellular fuel, energy storage, and structure. Two well-known examples of monosaccharides are glucose and fructose (Figure 4.1). Sucrose, another common sugar, is a disaccharide composed of one glucose and one fructose. Examples of long carbohydrate polymers include starch, the photosynthetic product of plants, and cellulose, the principle component of wood.

Lipids

Lipids are a diverse group of fatty or oily substances characterized by their insolubility in water and their solubility in fat solvents (e.g., ether, acetone, carbon tetrachloride, etc.). Like carbohydrates, lipids are molecules composed of C, H, and O, although they contain much more C and H relative to O. This high ratio of C and H relative to O accounts for the high energy output upon oxidation of lipids (Figure 4.2). Lipids form the major component of the plasma membrane and are involved in cellular communication.

Proteins

Proteins are large molecules ranging in molecular weight from about 5000 kiloDaltons (e.g., insulin) to 40 million kiloDaltons (e.g., tobacco mosaic virus protein). A protein is a polymer composed of a long chain of nitrogen-containing monomers known as *amino acids* linked together by *peptide bonds* (Figures 4.3 and 4.4). Proteins often bond with other complex molecules such as lipids, carbohydrates, nucleic acids, and heme groups to form more complex structures. Proteins exhibit a virtually unlimited variety of sizes and configurations due to:

1. The large number of amino acids that enter into the manufacture of a single protein molecule (thousands in many cases).

2. The almost infinite number of combinations the different amino acids can form.

3. The reactivity of side groups of the individual amino acids.

Proteins are unparalleled in the diversity of roles assumed in the maintenance of biological systems. They constitute up to 75% of the dry weight of cells and are a large component of the plasma membrane and organelles. In addition to their role in cell structure, proteins act as biological catalysts (enzymes), regulators of cell and tissue functions, and are involved in the immune response.

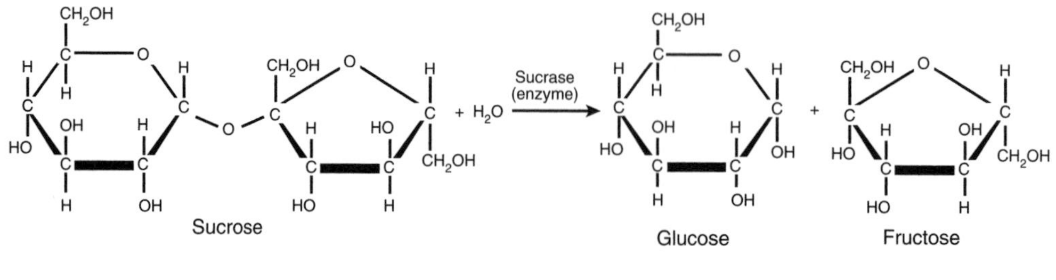

Figure 4.1. The Chemical Structures of Sucrose, Glucose, and Fructose

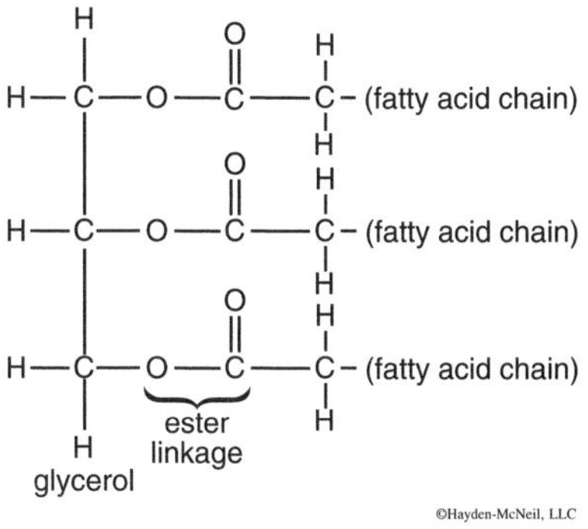

Figure 4.2. Structure of a Triglyceride

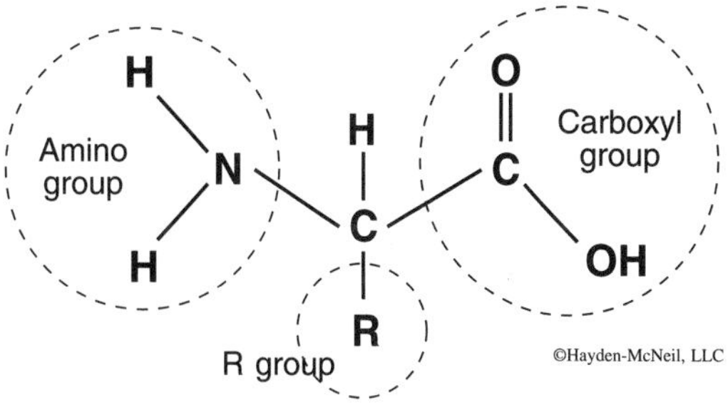

Figure 4.3. Structure of an Amino Acid

Common amino acids

Aspartic acid (Asp) I pH = 3.0	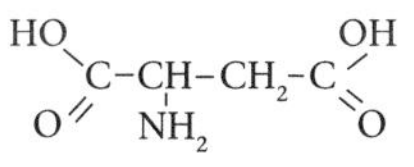	Alanine (Ala) I pH = 6.0	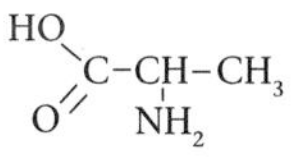
Glutamic acid (Glu) I pH = 3.2	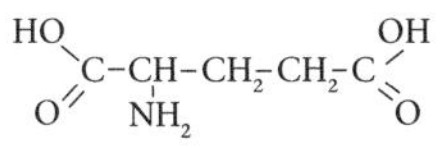	Glycine (Gly) I pH = 6.0	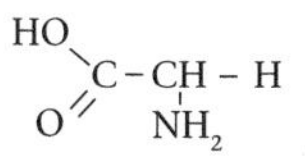
Cysteine (Cys) I pH = 5.0	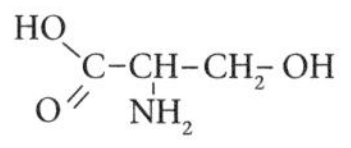	Leucine (Leu) I pH = 6.0	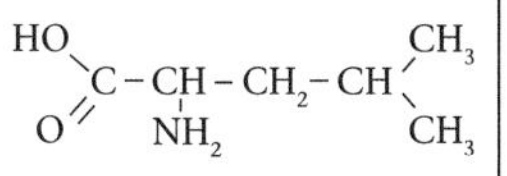
Asparagine (Asn) I pH = 5.4	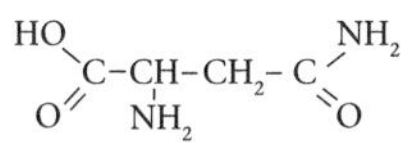	Valine (Val) I pH = 6.0	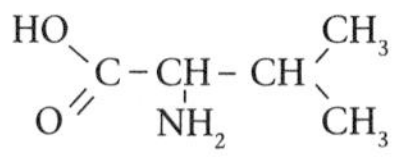
Phenylalanine (Phe) I pH = 5.5	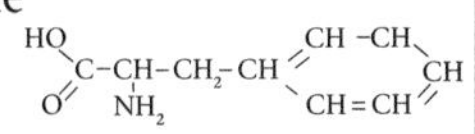	Isoleucine (Ilu) I pH = 6.1	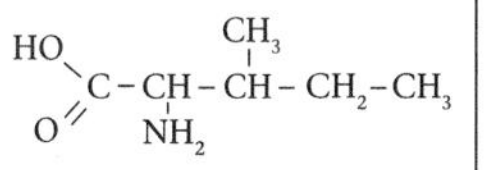
Glutamine (Gln) I pH = 5.7	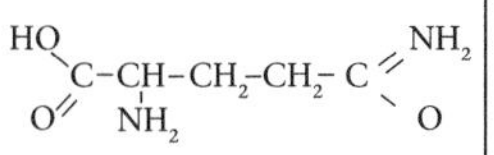	Proline (Pro) I pH = 6.3	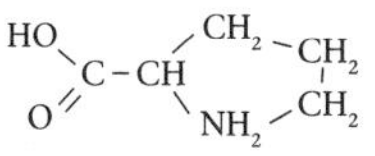
Serine (Ser) I pH = 5.7	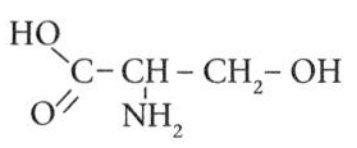	Threonine (Thr) I pH = 6.5	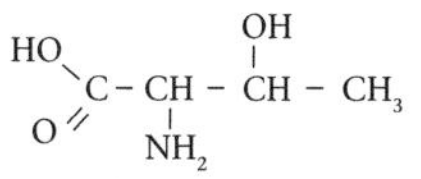
Tyrosine (Tyr) I pH = 5.7	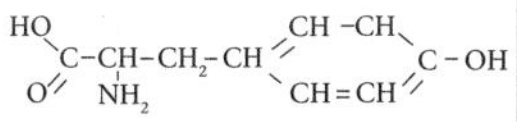	Histidine (His) I pH = 7.6	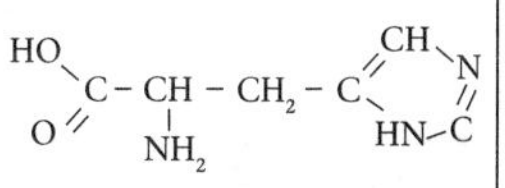
Methionine (Met) I pH = 5.8	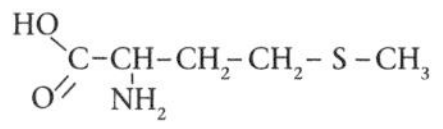	Lysine (Lys) I pH = 9.8	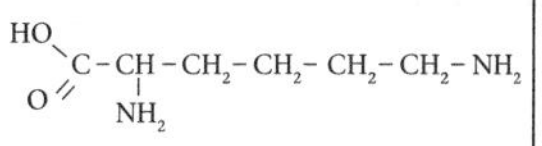
Tryptophan (Trp) I pH = 5.9	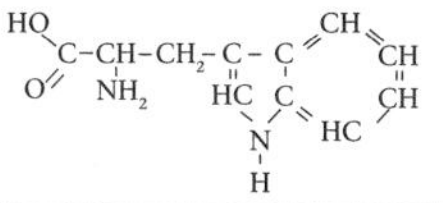	Arginine (Arg) I pH = 10.8	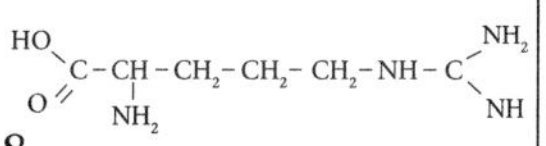

Figure 4.4. The 20 Common Amino Acids

Nucleic Acids

Nucleic acids are linear polymers of nucleotides, which function in the storage, utilization, and transmission of genetic information. There are two types of nucleic acids: *RNA* (ribonucleic acid) and *DNA* (deoxyribonucleic acid) (Figure 4.5). DNA molecules encode the "blueprints" for the manufacture of proteins. They are also involved in the continuance of genetic information from generation to generation. RNA molecules are involved in the manufacture of proteins through the processes of transcription and translation.

This lab will focus primarily on proteins and carbohydrates.

A. Lugol Test for Starch

Lugol solution is an indicator solution for starch. The iodine in the Lugol's solution forms a complex with starch molecules, which is bluish black in color. No change from the reddish-orange color of the Lugol solution is an indication that starch is not present.

1. Obtain two test tubes. Label them "1" and "2."

2. Add 5 ml of sucrose solution to test tube "1."

3. Add 5 ml of starch solution to test tube "2."

4. Add 5 drops of Lugol solution to each tube.

5. Mix and record the results.

6. Now take a section of potato and add Lugol solution. Is starch present in the potato? Next try it on an onion. Is starch present in the onion? What about an apple?

WARNING: Lugol solution contains iodine and is slightly toxic. It can also cause skin burns and permanently stain clothing.

B. Benedict's Test for Reducing Sugars

All monosaccharides, as well as some of the disaccharide sugars, possess the capacity to reduce alkaline solutions of copper. These monosaccharides and disaccharides are called **reducing sugars**. A reducing sugar is a sugar with actual or potential aldehyde or ketone groups. Benedict's solution is a mixture of $CuSO_4$, Na_2CO_3, and sodium citrate. During the reaction, a complex series of reactions occur, but the visible end result is that Cu^{2+} is reduced, causing a color change from blue to brick red (this is the positive result). The solution will remain blue if no reducing sugars are present (negative result).

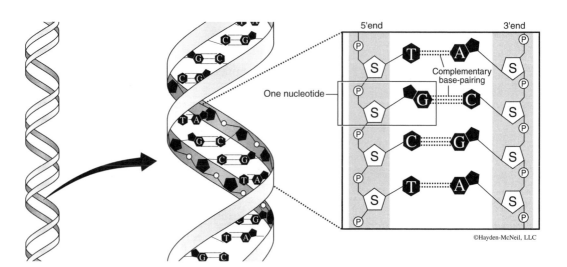

Figure 4.5. Structure of DNA

Obtain nine test tubes. Label them "1" through "9."

1. Add 3 ml of water to tube 1. This will be your control.

2. Add 3 ml of glucose solution to tube 2.

3. Add 3 ml of fructose solution to tube 3.

4. Add 3 ml of sucrose solution to tube 4.

5. Add 3 ml of starch solution to tube 5.

6. Add 3 ml of Sprite into tube 6.

7. Add 3 ml of Diet Sprite into tube 7.

8. Add 3 ml of milk into tube 8.

9. Add 3 ml of fruit juice to tube 9.

10. Add 3 ml of Benedict's solution to each of the nine tubes.

11. Place all tubes in a block heater for about 5 minutes.

WARNING: The block heater is 80°C and can cause severe burns. Be careful!

12. Check for color changes.

13. Record your results in Data Table 4.1.

WARNING: Benedict's solution contains copper sulfate and is toxic.

C. Identification of Amino Acids by Thin Layer Chromatography (TLC)

Ninhydrin reacts with amino acids to produce various shades of blue, purple, and yellow pigments. This reagent can be used as a qualitative test for amino acids and proteins. It was once widely used in forensics to detect fingerprints on paper, but has since been replaced by other, less toxic, chemicals.

PLATE PREPARATION

1. Only touch the corners of the plate with your hands as oils from your hands may stain the plate. Do not bend, crease, or scratch the plate.

2. With a pencil, draw a line 1 cm from the bottom of the plate. Do not push hard on the pencil when drawing the line.

3. Make marks 1 cm apart along the pencil line on the bottom of the plate. Be sure that the first and last marks are *at least* 1 cm from the edge of the plate.

SPOTTING

4. Find the first amino acid. Record in your lab book that this amino acid is spotted on mark 1.

5. Dip a capillary tube in the liquid containing the amino acid.

6. While holding the capillary tube perpendicular to the plate, gently touch the tip of the capillary tube on mark 1. Let a small amount of the liquid flow onto the plate. A wet spot should appear.

7. Place the capillary tube back into the side tube and return the bottle to the appropriate station.

8. Repeat steps 4–7 for each of the remaining bottles (the known amino acids and one unknown). All of the marks on your plate should have a spot.

9. Let the spots dry well.

RUNNING THE PLATE

10. Gently place the plate inside of the chromatography plate with long tweezers.

11. The chromatography chamber holds four plates.

12. Check the plate every few minutes. Be sure to have a pencil ready if you need to remove the plate.

13. Use the long tweezers to remove the plate from the chamber when the solvent has risen to within 1 cm from the top of the plate.

14. Immediately mark the leading edge of the solvent front. If you do not mark the solvent level, your plate will be worthless!

15. Let the plate dry.

DEVELOPING THE PLATE

16. Take the plate to the hood in the lab prep room (the room in the back of the lab).

17. Your TA will place the plates on a hot plate after soaking it with Ninhydrin—a chemical that reacts with amino acids to form a purple color (or yellow with proline).

CALCULATING Rf

18. Mark the center of each of the now visible amino acid spots.

19. Measure (in centimeters) the distance from the spot origin to the leading edge of the solvent.

20. Measure (in centimeters) the distance from the spot origin to the center of the spot.

21. Calculate Rf by dividing the distance traveled by the amino acid by the distance traveled by the solvent.

$$Rf = \frac{\text{Distance traveled by the amino acid}}{\text{Distance traveled by the solvent}}$$

22. Record the measured Rf values in Data Table 4.2.

23. Compare the Rf of the known amino acids to the Rf of the unknown.

BIOMOLECULES W O R K S H E E T

C H A P T E R 4

Name _____

Section _____

Date _____

Lugol Test for Starch

What was the result when you added the Lugol's solution to the following items?

Starch Solution: _____   Sucrose Solution: _____

Potato: _____   Onion: _____   49

Apple: _____

Benedict's Test for Reducing Sugars

Complete the Data Table below. Indicate those solutions that contain a reducing sugar.

Data Table 4.1. Results of the Benedict's Test for Nine Solutions

Solution	Color	Reducing Sugar Present or Absent?
Water		
Glucose		
Fructose		
Sucrose		
Starch		
Sprite		
Diet Sprite		
Milk		
Fruit juice		

Thin Layer Chromatography

Complete the following table. Use the Rf values measured for each known as the primary indicator for determining the identity of the unknown—only use color and shape as a secondary indicator.

Data Table 4.2. Rf Calculations for Six Known and One Unknown Amino Acid Samples

Spot	Rf Value	Color and Shape	Amino Acids Present
Histidine			
Alanine			
Proline			
Methionine			
Tyrosine			
Lysine			
Unknown—there will be three spots	spot 1. spot 2. spot 3.		

DETERMINATION OF THE PROPERTIES OF THE ENZYME TURNIP PEROXIDASE

C H A P T E R   5

When this lab is completed, students should be able to do the following:

- Define the following: enzyme, activation energy, active site, substrate, product, reaction rate, and enzyme activity.

- Explain the effects of changes in enzyme concentration, temperature, and pH on enzyme function.

- Discuss the effects of a competitive inhibitor on enzyme function.

- Improve data collection and analysis skills.

Enzymes are biological catalysts, which speed up or regulate the rate of chemical reactions by lowering the energy necessary for the reaction to proceed. The energy input necessary to drive a reaction is known as the **activation energy** (Figure 5.1). Many biological reactions are spontaneous and would occur if left alone, but they would proceed at a pace that is much too slow for the organism's needs. With the presence of enzymes, however, the reaction rates of biochemical reactions are increased to a rate that is acceptable for life functions.

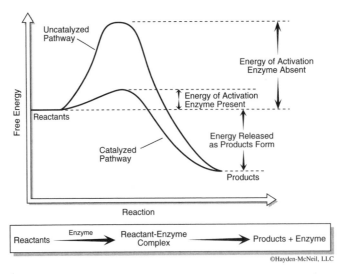

Figure 5.1. The Energy States of Enzyme-Catalyzed and Non-Enzyme-Catalyzed Reactions

In an enzyme-catalyzed reaction, the molecules that are reacting are known as the **substrates** and those formed are known as the **products**. Most enzymes are proteins (recently, RNA molecules with catalytic properties have been discovered). The shape of the enzyme is crucial for its function. On every enzyme is an **active site**—a binding site for the substrates. If the enzyme collided with the substrates in the proper orientation, an **enzyme-substrate complex** will form (Figure 5.2). The active site of the enzyme will strain and weaken the bonds of the substrates to more easily allow the reaction to proceed. When the substrates have reacted, the products formed will be released from the active site by the enzyme. The enzyme remains unchanged by the reaction and is free to catalyze the next substrates it encounters.

The rate at which the enzyme can convert substrate to product is known as the **reaction rate** or **enzyme activity**. If the shape of the enzyme is changed, it may affect substrate binding which will, in turn, affect enzyme activity. Two environmental factors commonly affecting enzyme shape are **temperature** and **pH**. Temperature is simply a measure of molecular motion. In most reactions, if the temperature is increased, the faster moving molecules will have more kinetic energy and the overall rate of the reaction will increase. The same is true for enzyme-catalyzed

reactions, but only to a point. As temperature is increased, the frequency of collisions and the average energy of the enzymes and substrates increase. The increased molecular motion in the enzyme, however, can affect the shape of the active site. If the temperature is increased too much, the shape of the active site will change and no longer function. This will cause the enzyme to become **denatured**. You can think of this as the enzyme shaking too much and becoming unraveled. With the enzyme inactive, its catalytic properties are gone and the reaction rate will dramatically be reduced.

The temperature at which the enzyme functions at the greatest efficiency is known as the **temperature optimum** or T_{opt}. In most organisms, the temperature optimum is a temperature slightly greater than the typical body temperature. For example, the average body temperature of a human is 37°C (98.6°F). Our enzymes have T_{opt}s of about 41°C. This allows our bodies to have enzymes that normally function near the point of peak efficiency, but also gives some leeway if the body temperature should rise due to exercise or fever. If one's body temperature rises too much, their enzymes will be denatured and the organism may die. Organisms that cannot regulate body temperature as efficiently as mammals, such as reptiles, plants, and bacteria,

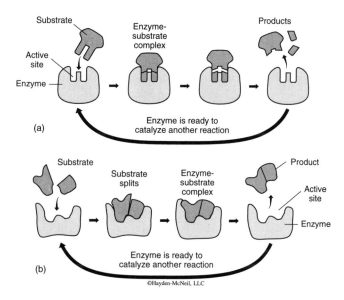

Figure 5.2. The Formation of Enzyme-Substrate Complexes

have enzymes with T_{opt}s much higher than ours. This gives them a much greater environmental tolerance to compensate for their lack of ability to regulate their body temperatures. The drawback, however, is their enzymes are typically exposed to conditions far removed from their optimum and may not function as efficiently as those in mammals.

Since most enzymes are proteins, changes in pH will most likely affect the interactions of the R-groups. Enzymes constructed with many acidic or basic amino acids in the active site will be very pH sensitive while those without will be less so. As with temperature, enzymes have a **pH optimum** at which they function at peak efficiency. At pH's greater or lesser than this pH_{opt}, enzymes will have lower activity. In most organisms, the pH_{opt} of an enzyme is the pH of the environment at which it will typically function. For example, an enzyme that functions in the blood will have a pH_{opt} of approximately 7.4, the pH of the blood, while an enzyme that functions in the stomach will have a pH_{opt} much lower since the stomach is acidic.

The binding of substrate to enzyme is very specific. The geometry of the active site is such that typically only the substrates can bind. However, sometimes other molecules have shapes similar to that of a substrate and can also bind to the active site. If this other molecule is present with the substrates, then the enzyme will form enzyme-substrate complexes with both the proper substrate and the other molecule. Since the additional molecule blocks the binding of the proper substrate to the active site, it is called a **competitive inhibitor**.

Turnip Peroxidase

In this lab you will be observing some of the properties of the enzyme **turnip peroxidase**. As you may have guessed, this enzyme is a peroxidase found in a turnip. A turnip is a plant that has a large underground storage root rich in this enzyme. Peroxidases are a class of enzyme that breaks down hydrogen peroxide (H_2O_2), a highly reactive byproduct of metabolism, into water (H_2O) and oxygen gas (O_2). The reaction is given below:

$$2\,H_2O_2 \xrightarrow{\text{Peroxidase}} 2\,H_2O + 2\,O^{\bullet}$$

The oxygen free radicals ($O^{\bullet}$) formed often react with each other to form oxygen gas (O_2) or other secondary compounds.

Since the concentration of water is very difficult to measure, we will use the production of the free radical of oxygen as a means to measure the reaction rate. This is typically done by coupling the first reaction with a second reaction involving the oxygen. Catechol, a chemical typically found in plants, is easily oxidized by the free radicals of oxygen. In the presence of oxygen free radicals, electrons and hydrogens are removed from catechol and it is converted to benzoquinone, a pigment product. The hydrogens and electrons removed then combine with oxygen, forming water. The pigment products are responsible for the darkening of fruits and vegetables, such as apples and potatoes, after exposure to air.

$$Catechol + O^{\bullet} \rightarrow Benzoquinone + H_2O$$

In our experimental procedure, we will use a high initial concentration of reduced catechol so that we can ensure that when a free radical of oxygen is formed, it will immediately react with the catechol, forming the more highly oxidized benzoquinone. The rate of the second reaction is dependent upon the production of oxygen free radicals formed in the first reaction. For example, if oxygen free radical production doubles, the oxidation of catechol will also double. Since catechol is clear and benzoquinone is brown-colored, the rate of benzoquinone can be easily detected using a spectrophotometer. **Dye-coupled** reactions such as these are an easy way to determine chemical reaction rates and are commonly used in biology. We will use a spectrophotometer to measure the production of oxidized catechol and use this rate as a proxy for peroxidase activity.

Preparation of Turnip Peroxidase Extract

Your TA will prepare the crude turnip enzyme extract. However, the concentration of peroxidase in turnips is not constant. It fluctuates due to season, ripeness, and the genetic make-up of the turnip. You must therefore standardize the amount of extract that you will use for the rest of the experiment. What you are looking for is the concentration of enzyme that will quickly catalyze the breakdown of H_2O_2, but not too quickly. If too little enzyme extract is used, the reaction will proceed too slowly and your accuracy will be compromised. If too much extract is used, all of the H_2O_2 will be consumed and

the reaction will stop, again compromising your ability to accurately measure reaction rate. Like Goldilocks, you are looking for the concentration of enzyme extract that is not too fast, not too slow, but just right.

The following conventions will hold true for any portion of this experiment. Tube 1 will be the blank. It will contain a pH buffer, catechol, and H_2O_2. Reaction tubes will be prepared in pairs. One pair will contain pH buffer and enzyme extract, while the other pair will contain catechol and H_2O_2. As long as they remain separate, they are stable. To start the reaction, you must thoroughly mix the two tubes. Doing so will enable the enzyme in the extract to react with the H_2O_2, creating the oxygen free radical that will react with the catechol. Be sure that before you mix the tubes, you obtain a square of Parafilm. When mixing, place the Parafilm over the top and invert the tube twice. Do not shake the mixed tube—this will create bubbles, which will interfere with the spectrophotometer.

1. Obtain approximately 50 ml of turnip enzyme extract and approximately 50 ml of 3% H_2O_2 from your TA. Place these in the beakers labeled "Enzyme" and "H_2O_2". Note that the beaker labeled "Enzyme" has a pink tape label and the beaker labeled "H_2O_2" has a white tape label. Be sure that you only use the pink and white pipettes when measuring out your solutions so that there will be no contamination.

2. You should already have a bottle of pH buffer (with a green tape label) and catechol (with an orange tape label) at your table. Find the appropriately labeled pipettes and rinse all of them out to ensure that you will not contaminate any of your reaction tubes.

3. Obtain seven test tubes and label them 1–7. Use Table 5.1 on the next page to prepare the seven test tubes.

4. Set the spectrophotometer to 500 nm, the λ_{max} of benzoquinone.

Table 5.1. Preparation of the Standardization of Turnip Peroxidase Extract (all volumes in ml)

Tube	Buffer (pH 5)	Extract	H_2O_2	Catechol	Total Volume
1 (Blank)	5.0	—	2.0	1.0	8.0
2	4.5	0.5	—	—	5.0
3	—	—	2.0	1.0	3.0
4	4.0	1.0	—	—	5.0
5	—	—	2.0	1.0	3.0
6	3.0	2.0	—	—	5.0
7	—	—	2.0	1.0	3.0

5. Select one group member to be the mixer, one to be the timer, and one to be the data recorder. Blank the spectrophotometer at 500 nm using tube 1. Mix tubes 2 and 3 (the standardization of 0.5 ml of extract), wipe off the cuvette, and place in the spectrophotometer. Begin timing when the reaction tube is placed in the spectrophotometer. Leave the reaction tube in the spec and record absorbance every 20 seconds for two minutes in Data Table 5.1. Note that you do not need to blank after each measurement. The spectrophotometers will remain stable for the two minutes you will be taking data.

6. When complete with taking data for the 0.5 ml of extract sample, reblank the spectrophotometer and repeat the above procedure with tubes 4 and 5, the standardization of 1.0 ml of extract. When complete with this, reblank and repeat with tubes 6 and 7, the standardization of 2.0 ml of extract.

7. Make a quick plot of the data you have just recorded on Data Table 5.1. Observe the general trends of the data—use a ruler and estimate a best-fit line for the linear portion of the data. Be sure to note if the data sets tend to plateau at the ends—if it does so, this indicates that the reaction is proceeding to completion. You are looking for the concentration of enzyme extract with the steepest slope that does not level off.

8. Once you have decided which concentration of enzyme extract will be used, talk to your TA about how you will perform the next steps of the experiment. *If you are using 2.0 ml of the enzyme, you will have to modify your experimental protocol.*

Factors Affecting Enzyme Activity: Temperature, pH, and Competitive Inhibitors
TEMPERATURE EFFECTS ON ENZYME ACTIVITY

Temperature is an indicator of molecular motion. In most cases, an increase in temperature will promote an increase in the rate of a reaction. However, in enzyme-catalyzed reactions, too much molecular motion will destroy the catalytic ability of the enzyme and dramatically reduce the reaction rate. The temperature at which the enzyme functions at its greatest capacity is known as its temperature optimum (T_{opt}). In this portion of the experiment, you will perform the reaction at five different temperatures and determine the T_{opt} of turnip peroxidase.

To complete this portion of the experiment, prepare reaction tubes as indicated in Table 5.2 and follow the procedure below. Be sure that you initially rinse out your pipettes and that you are using the appropriately colored pipettes to prevent contamination.

1. Place the *unmixed* reaction tubes in the appropriate environmental conditions. For 4°C, place tubes 2 and 3 in an ice bucket. For 23°C, room temperature, no temperature modification is necessary. For 32°C, 48°C, and 72°C, you will need to place the *unmixed* tubes in the appropriate heating block.

2. Observe and record the actual temperatures of the heating blocks. Every effort has been made to ensure that the heating blocks are at the indicated temperatures, but sometimes they are off by a degree or two. This should have little effect on the experiment, but to ensure accuracy, you should record the actual temperature of your samples.

3. Let the unmixed tubes sit for at least five minutes. The room temperature tubes may be used immediately, but the others must come to temperature equilibrium. You may use the thermometer to check the temperatures of the reaction tubes—just be sure that you rinse off the thermometers before and after measurements to ensure that there is no contamination.

4. When a set of reaction tubes have come to temperature equilibrium, you may begin. Blank the spectrophotometer at 500 nm using Tube 1. Mix the two reaction tubes and invert twice using Parafilm. Be sure you wipe off the tube before placing in the spectrophotometer—excess moisture on the cuvette will affect the spectrophotometer's reading.

5. Take an absorbance reading every twenty seconds for two minutes. Record the data in the appropriate column in Data Table 5.2. When completed, remove the reaction tube, reblank the spectrophotometer, and repeat the above procedure for the next reaction tubes.

pH Effects on Enzyme Activity

Like temperature, pH can affect enzyme shape. The three-dimensional shape of an enzyme may be stabilized by interactions between acidic and/or basic R-groups. Additionally, amino acids in the active site may have acidic or basic R-groups. Changes in pH may alter the configuration of these amino acids, affecting their ability to maintain enzyme active site geometry or bind to substrates. Ultimately, these changes may affect the enzymes catalytic ability. In this portion of the exercise, you will measure the enzyme activity at four different pH's and determine the pH_{opt} for turnip peroxidase.

To complete this portion of the experiment, prepare reaction tubes as indicated in Table 5.3 and follow the procedure on the next page. Be sure that you initially rinse out your pipettes and that you are using the appropriately colored pipette to prevent contamination.

1. Blank the spectrophotometer at 500 nm using Tube 1. Take tubes 2 and 3, the pH 3 series, and mix the two reaction tubes by inverting twice using Parafilm. Be sure you wipe off the tube before placing in the spectrophotometer—excess moisture on the cuvette will affect the spectrophotometer's reading.

Table 5.2. Preparation for the Effects of Temperature on Turnip Peroxidase Activity (all volumes in ml)

Temperature	Tube	Buffer (pH 5)	Extract	H_2O_2	Catechol	Total Volume
	1 (blank)	5.0	—	2.0	1.0	8.0
4°C	2	4.0*	1.0*	—	—	5.0
	3	—	—	2.0	1.0	3.0
23°C	4	4.0*	1.0*	—	—	5.0
	5	—	—	2.0	1.0	3.0
32°C	6	4.0*	1.0*	—	—	5.0
	7	—	—	2.0	1.0	3.0
48°C	8	4.0*	1.0*	—	—	5.0
	9	—	—	2.0	1.0	3.0
72°C	10	4.0*	1.0*	—	—	5.0
	11	—	—	2.0	1.0	3.0

* These volumes assume you chose 1.0 ml of extract in the standardization portion of the experiment—if you chose 0.5 ml or 2.0 ml of extract, adjust the volume of extract and buffer accordingly so that they total 5.0 ml.

3.0ml 2.0mL

2. Take an absorbance reading every twenty seconds for two minutes. Record the data in the appropriate column in Data Table 5.3. When completed, remove the reaction tube, reblank the spectrophotometer, and repeat the above procedure for the next reaction tubes.

The Effects of a Competitive Inhibitor on Enzyme Activity

Hydroxylamine (HONH$_2$) has a chemical structure similar to hydrogen peroxide (H$_2$O$_2$). Both possess the ability to bind to the iron ion in the active site of turnip peroxidase. When hydroxylamine is bound to the active site, it prevents hydrogen peroxide from binding, thus lowering enzyme activity. This portion of the experiment will study the effects of hyrdoxylamine on turnip peroxidase activity.

To complete this portion of the experiment, prepare reaction tubes as indicated in Table 5.4 and follow the procedure below. Be sure that you initially rinse out your pipettes and that you are using the appropriately colored pipette to prevent contamination.

1. Blank the spectrophotometer at 500 nm using Tube 1. Take tubes 2 and 3, the uninhibited enzyme series, and mix the two reaction tubes

by inverting twice using Parafilm. Be sure you wipe off the tube before placing in the spectrophotometer—excess moisture on the cuvette will affect the spectrophotometer's reading.

2. Take an absorbance reading every twenty seconds for two minutes. Record the data in the appropriate column in Data Table 5.4. When completed, remove the reaction tube, reblank the spectrophotometer, and repeat the above procedure for the next reaction tubes. Be sure that when you prepare tubes 4 and 5, you use the enzyme extract that has been pre-mixed with hydroxylamine.

Data Analysis

The analysis of the data in this experiment will be very graph-intensive. Be sure you review the instructions on how to make graphs in Appendix A and review the online tutorial if you have any further questions. *All graphs must be generated using Excel or another spreadsheet. No hand-drawn graphs will be accepted!* Additionally, students are required to prepare their own graphs. Using a graph prepared by a lab partner is a violation of the University Academic Dishonesty Policy and persons doing so will be severely punished. See Appendix A for more details on how to prepare the graphs.

Table 5.3. Preparation for the Effects of pH on Turnip Peroxidase Activity (all volumes in ml)

pH	Tube	Buffer	Extract	H$_2$O$_2$	Catechol	Total Volume
	1 (blank)	5.0 (pH 5)	—	2.0	1.0	8.0
3	2	4.0* (pH 3)	1.0*	—	—	5.0
	3	—	—	2.0	1.0	3.0
5	4	4.0* (pH 5)	1.0*	—	—	5.0
	5	—	—	2.0	1.0	3.0
7	6	4.0* (pH 7)	1.0*	—	—	5.0
	7	—	—	2.0	1.0	3.0
9	8	4.0* (pH 9)	1.0*	—	—	5.0
	9	—	—	2.0	1.0	3.0

These volumes assume you chose 1.0 ml of extract in the standardization portion of the experiment—if you chose 0.5 ml or 2.0 ml of extract, adjust the volume of extract and buffer accordingly so that they total 5.0 ml.

Table 5.4. Preparation for the Effects of Hydroxylamine, a Competitive Inhibitor, on Turnip Peroxidase Activity (all volumes in ml)

Tube	Buffer (pH 5)	Extract	Hydroxylamine Treated Extract	H$_2$O$_2$	Catechol	Total Volume
1 (blank)	5.0	—	—	2.0	1.0	8.0
2	4.0*	1.0*	—	—	—	5.0
3	—	—	—	2.0	1.0	3.0
4	4.0*	—	1.0*	—	—	5.0
5	—	—	—	2.0	1.0	3.0

* These volumes assume you chose 1.0 ml of extract in the standardization portion of the experiment—if you chose 0.5 ml or 2.0 ml of extract, adjust the volume of extract and buffer accordingly so that they total 5.0 ml.

ANALYSIS OF TEMPERATURE DATA

Prepare a scatter plot of the data in Data Table 5.2. Look at the data—do any of the data sets plateau? If so, you may want to exclude these points from your analysis. Exclusion of data is not something to be taken lightly, however, so make sure that your data really are forming a plateau and not just possessing an aberrant data point. Have the spreadsheet generate a best-fit straight line for each temperature. Record the equation of the line in Data Table 5.5. The equation is written in the form y = ax + b. The cofactor before the x is the slope of the line—the slope of the line is also a measure of the enzyme activity (reaction rate). Record the reaction rate for each temperature in the appropriate column in Data Table 5.5.

Now prepare a scatter plot using the data found in Data Table 5.5. The x-coordinate for each data point will be the temperature. The y-coordinate for each data point will be the reaction rate of the enzyme at that temperature. Have the spreadsheet generate a smooth-flowing curve (do *not* have it connect the dots with straight lines—this will not accurately generate your T$_{opt}$). The highest point of the curve will be the T$_{opt}$ of turnip peroxidase. Note that it is highly unlikely that your T$_{opt}$ will be one of the measured temperatures. Instead, it will most likely be between two of the temperatures. This is why we generate the smooth-flowing curve.

ANALYSIS OF pH DATA

Preparation of the pH data is very similar to the preparation of the temperature data. Prepare a scatter plot of the data found in Data Table 5.3. Generate best-fit straight lines, again making sure that the data are not leveling off and forming a plateau. Have the spreadsheet generate the equations of each of the four lines and record these and the slopes of each line in Data Table 5.6.

Prepare a scatter plot of the data found in Data Table 5.6. The x-coordinate will be the pH of the system and the y-coordinate will be the reaction rate at that pH. Generate a smooth-flowing curve and determine the pH$_{opt}$.

ANALYSIS OF INHIBITOR DATA

Prepare a graph of the inhibitor data found in Data Table 5.4. Generate best-fit lines, making sure that the data are not leveling off and forming a plateau. Generate best-fit lines and fill in the equations and the slopes of both lines in Data Table 5.7.

To determine the percent inhibition of hydroxylamine on turnip peroxidase activity, use the equation below:

$$\left[\frac{(\text{Reaction Rate}_{normal} - \text{Reaction Rate}_{inhibited})}{\text{Reaction Rate}_{normal}} \right] * 100$$

DIFFUSION AND OSMOSIS

CHAPTER 6

After completing this laboratory, you should be able to:

- Describe the mechanism of diffusion at the molecular level.

- Discuss how several factors affect the rate of diffusion.

- Define *hypertonic*, *hypotonic*, and *isotonic* in terms of relative concentration differences with special reference to cells.

- Discuss how the cell wall and central vacuole act to maintain turgor pressure in plants.

- Explain how osmosis and osmoregulation are critical to maintaining homeostasis in cells.

- Apply the principles of osmosis to applications in ecology and medicine.

The cytoplasm and extracellular environment of cells are aqueous solutions, composed of water, which is the **solvent** or dissolving agent, and **solutes**, which are particles dissolved in the solvent. Organelle and plasma membranes are **semipermeable** (selectively permeable) membranes—certain substances can cross the membrane unaided while other substances cannot. Small molecules such as water, oxygen, and carbon dioxide, may freely cross cellular membranes by **diffusion**, a physical process in which molecules move from areas of high concentration to areas of low concentration. Think of what would happen if you put some food coloring into a flask of water (Figure 6.1). The food coloring would initially be concentrated in one area, but over time, the color would spread out. If you waited overnight, the color would be homogenous. The dye would have diffused throughout the entire flask. The energy that drives this movement is derived from the intrinsic kinetic energy found in all molecules above absolute zero. If nothing interferes, a solution will continue to diffuse until it reaches a steady state (the point at which molecules are still in motion, but more or less uniformly distributed).

Figure 6.1. Diffusion of a Dye in a Solution of Water

Larger hydrophobic molecules can cross a cellular membrane with difficulty while larger hydrophilic molecules, such as glucose, and charged particles of any size cannot cross without the aid of carrier proteins or molecular channels. Cells, however, need to be able to move ions and large molecules across their membranes. This is commonly achieved through the use of **facilitated diffusion** carrier proteins or through **active transport**. Facilitated diffusion utilizes very selective carrier proteins to allow entry of large molecules. The carrier proteins usually have two conformations, one open to the outside of the membrane and one open to the inside of the membrane. They are selective, so they only allow one type of molecule to bind to it. Think of a facilitated diffusion carrier protein as a door that only allows one type of person to enter or leave a room (for example, women with red hair). Everyone can see the door, but only red-headed women may use it. The binding of a solute to a carrier protein usually causes a conformation change, opening the molecule on the other side of the membrane. Note that facilitated diffusion carrier proteins work in both directions—the net direction of movement of solutes across the membrane will depend upon the relative concentration differences across the membrane.

Unlike facilitated diffusion, active transport requires energy, usually in the form of ATP. Highly selective carrier proteins with two conformations are involved again, but ATP must be used to alter the conformation and allow the solutes to cross the membrane.

Osmosis is a special form of diffusion. During osmosis, water moves from areas where it is highly concentrated to areas where it has a low concentration. Differences in the cellular concentration of water are created through the presence of solutes that cannot cross a membrane. These **osmotically active solutes** bind to several water molecules, effectively lowering the relative concentration of water. Since the solutes cannot cross the membrane, water will cross until there is equilibrium. Three terms, **hypertonic**, **hypotonic**, and **isotonic** are used when referring to any two solutions separated by a semipermeable membrane (Figure 6.2). The hypertonic solution has the higher concentration of osmotically active solutes than the solution on the other side of the membrane (*hyper* means more, *tonic* refers to the osmotically active solutes). A hypotonic solution has a lower concentration of osmotically active solutes than the other solution (*hypo* means under or less). When two solutions have equal amounts of osmotically active solutes, the solution is in equilibrium and is said to be isotonic (*iso* means same). The net flow of water is from a hypotonic solution to a hypertonic solution. When the solutions become isotonic, there is no net flow of water. Note that these terms are relative to each other—if a cell is placed in pure water, the water is hypotonic to the cell cytoplasm while the cytoplasm is hypertonic to the water. In biology, however, most applications of the terms hypotonic and hypertonic refer to the solution in which a cell is immersed.

Movement of water from a hypotonic solution to a hypertonic solution produces a force. The swelling of a cell when placed in a hypotonic solution is a result of this force—the rushing in of water stretches the plasma membrane. The net flow of water, however, can be prevented by the application of a force that prevents further expansion of the membrane. The amount of force required to prevent the net flow of water is known as the **osmotic pressure**. A plant cell is surrounded by a rigid cell wall and contains a central vacuole, which is hypertonic to the surrounding medium. There is almost always a potential net flow of water into the plant cell, causing it to swell. When the cell swells to the volume encompassed by the cell wall, the rigid cell wall resists further swelling. This resistance, known as **turgor pressure**, is what supports the plant (Figure 6.2). Think of what happens when you don't water a plant—it wilts. The wilting is due to a loss of turgor pressure. The central vacuole usually is still hypertonic, but there isn't enough water present in the system to create the necessary turgor pressure to resist gravity, so wilting occurs. If you water the plant, water flows in, turgor pressure can be restored and maintained, and the leaf will again resist gravity.

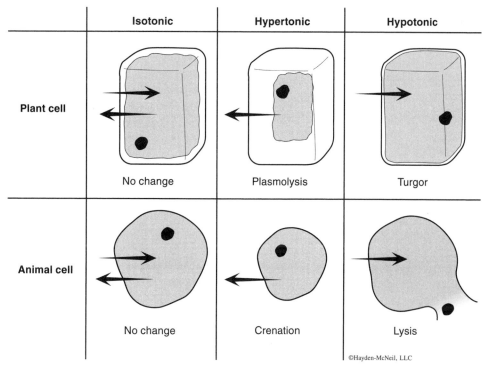

Figure 6.2. *The Effects of Changes in Osmolarity in Plant and Animal Cells*

Study of Osmosis and Diffusion Through a Semipermeable Membrane

This experiment will study the flow of both solutes and water through a semipermeable membrane. The membrane you will use is a piece of dialysis tubing. When a person's kidney fails, they must undergo dialysis to filter the blood, and dialysis tubing is used in this process. The membrane of dialysis tubing is semipermeable, allowing molecules smaller than the pore size (typically 14 kiloDaltons) to freely pass while preventing the flow of larger molecules. In this experiment, you will place a solution of known tonicity (concentration) in a sac made from dialysis tubing and immerse this sac in another solution of known tonicity. You will examine the net flow of solutes and water into and out of the sac over the course of an hour using indicator tests.

Procedure

Obtain a 15 cm strip of dialysis tubing. It will be soaking in water to make the membrane more flexible. Take one end of the tubing and fold it once and then back again, forming an S-shape. Take one of the two plastic clips and clip the S-shape, sealing one end of the bag. Pipette out approximately 15 ml of a prepared solution containing a mixture of 3% BSA and 1.0 M NaCl. BSA is short for Bovine Serum Albumin, a solution of protein obtained from the plasma of cows commonly used in biology. Form another S-shape at the other end of the dialysis tubing, taking care to force excess air out of the tubing and leaving at least 1 cm of space between the clip and the solution so that there is room for water to flow into the sac if necessary. Blot the dialysis tubing sac dry and then take the weight. You are going to use the weight of the sac as an indicator of the net movement of water. An increase in weight at the end of the experiment will indicate a net flow of water into the sac while a decrease in weight at the end of the experiment will indicate a net flow of water out of the sac.

After weighing the sac, pour approximately 200 ml of a solution containing 0.25 M Na_2SO_4 and 0.25% starch solution into a plastic beaker. Place the dialysis tubing sac in the starch/Na_2SO_4 solution and allow it to sit for one hour. When you are done, your setup should look like Figure 6.3.

What do you predict will happen to the total volume of water in the dialysis sac? Will it increase? Decrease? Remain the same? Defend your answer.

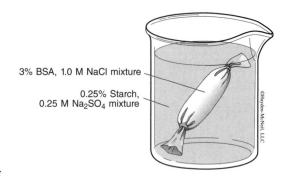

3% BSA, 1.0 M NaCl mixture

0.25% Starch, 0.25 M Na_2SO_4 mixture

Figure 6.3. Experimental Setup for Osmosis and Diffusion Experiment

While waiting for the solutions inside and outside the sac to come to equilibrium, you will test the solutions inside the sac and outside the sac for the presence of Na^+, protein, SO_4^{2-}, and starch using the procedure outlined below.

1. Obtain eight 10 ml test tubes.

2. Number four of the tubes 1–4 and place 3.0 ml of the BSA/NaCl stock solution in each of the four tubes. This is the **inside start** solution in Data Table 6.1 since it represents the solution placed *inside* the dialysis tubing sac at the *start* of the experiment.

3. Number the four remaining tubes 1–4 and place 3.0 ml of the Starch/Na_2SO_4 stock solution in each of the four tubes. This is the **outside start** solution in Data Table 6.1.

4. Test for Cl^- ion: Obtain a dropper bottle of $AgNO_3$ and place two drops of $AgNO_3$ in tube 1 of the inside start and outside start solutions. If Cl^- is present, the Ag^{2+} will react with it, forming $AgCl_2$, which is a milky white precipitate. Record the presence (+) or absence (−) of $AgCl_2$ in Data Table 6.1. *Caution:* $AgNO_3$ will stain your clothing and skin.

5. Test for SO_4^{2-}: Obtain a dropper bottle of $BaCl_2$ and place two drops into tube 3 of inside start and outside start solutions. If SO_4^{2-} is present, the Ba^{2+} will react with it, forming $BaSO_4$, which is a milky white precipitate. Record your results in Data Table 6.1.

6. Test for Starch: Place two drops of Lugol's solution into tube 4 both inside start and outside start solutions. Shake liberally and observe for a minute. If starch is present, the solution will turn a bluish-black color. Record your results in Data Table 6.1.

7. Test for Protein: Your TA will give you two Albustix. Albustix are detector strips used by diabetics to detect pH, protein concentration, and other dissolved solutes in their urine. Your TA will instruct you on which detector square is the protein test. Place one Albustix in each of the two tube 2's and allow it to sit for two minutes. If protein is present, the detector square will turn green.

8. After one hour, remove the dialysis sac from the solution and blot it dry. Weigh the dialysis sac. Any change in weight will be due to water entering or leaving the bag (while it is possible for the ions or macromolecules to enter and leave, their additional weight is insignificant compared to the weight of water entering or leaving). Record your results in Data Table 6.1.

9. Obtain eight 10 ml test tubes.

10. Open the dialysis sac and remove four 3.0 ml solutions, placing each in a test tube labeled 1–4 **inside end**. These will represent the solution found inside the sac at the end of the experiment.

11. With the dialysis sac removed, gently stir the solution remaining in the beaker. Remove four 3.0 ml solutions, placing each in an empty tube labeled 1–4 **outside end**. These will represent the solution found outside the sac at the end of the experiment.

12. Repeat the four tests (Cl^-, protein, SO_4^{2-}, starch) by following the procedure outlined in steps 4–7. Record your results in Data Table 6.1

Any change in condition from start to finish will reflect a solute moving from one side of the sac to the other during the course of the experiment.

PLASMOLYSIS IN ELODEA

Elodea is a freshwater aquatic plant commonly studied in biology laboratories. Aquatic plants usually have thinner cell walls because water is a much more buoyant medium than air and the maintenance of turgor pressure is not as significant as in terrestrial plants. However, the principles of osmoregulation still apply to aquatic plants. When a plant cell is placed in a hypertonic medium, water will leave the central vacuole, causing the plasma membrane to shrink away from the cell wall. The reduction of total cell volume is known as **plasmolysis** (Figure 6.2).

Obtain a growing leaf tip from an *Elodea* plant. Prepare a wet mount of the leaf tip and observe it under medium power. The plasma membranes should be flush up against the cell wall. Now, without removing the slide, place a drop of 35% sucrose solution on the edge of the coverslip. The addition of the sucrose will make the surrounding medium hypertonic. After a few minutes, what do you observe has happened to the cell? What do you hypothesize would happen if you placed another drop of pure water on the coverslip edge and waited a few minutes? Why do you think this?

DIFFUSION IN GELS

Diffusion is the movement of molecules from areas of high concentration to areas of low concentration. The energy for this process is derived from the intrinsic kinetic energy found in all molecules. Several factors can affect the rate of diffusion in a medium. First, the **temperature** of a system will affect the rate of diffusion. Temperature is a measure of molecular motion—the greater the temperature, the greater the molecular motion. A system at a higher temperature will have faster moving molecules, which will lead to a greater rate of diffusion.

Molecular weight of the diffusing molecules will also affect diffusion rate. Recall from physics that kinetic energy is $\frac{1}{2}mv^2$. Imagine two molecules, one large and one small, are at the same temperature. They will have the same kinetic energy, but since kinetic energy is based both upon mass and velocity, the heavier molecule will be moving more slowly than the lighter molecule. Therefore, at the same temperature, a heavier molecule will have a lower rate of diffusion than a lighter molecule.

The medium in which the molecules are diffusing can also affect the rate of diffusion. Interactions due to polarity, charge, and even molecular shape, can affect diffusion rate.

In this experiment, you will observe the rate of diffusion of three dyes in a 1% agar solution in a system at room temperature and again in a system that is placed on ice.

Obtain two Petri plates containing 1% agar poured to a depth of 5 mm. Use a drinking straw to make three wells equally spaced in both plates (note: you must remove the agar plug leaving the 5 mm hole in the agar). To one well in each plate, fill the well with methyl blue dye. To a second well in both plates, fill the well with methyl orange. Finally to the last well in both plates, fill the well with congo red. **CAUTION**: *These dyes produce permanent stains in clothes*. Place one of the plates on your lab bench and carefully place the other plate on ice. Let the agar sit for at least an hour.

After an hour, measure how far each dye has moved in each agar plate. Record these data. You may then dispose of the agar plates in the garbage.

68

The following data may be of use to answer the questions on the diffusion in gels exercise in the homework:

	Methyl Blue	**Congo Red**	**Methyl Orange**
Chemical Formula	$C_{37}H_{27}N_3O_9S_3Na_2$	$C_{32}H_{22}N_6O_6S_2Na_2$	$4\text{-}NaOSO_2C_6H_4N{:}NC_6H_4\text{-}(CH_3)_2$
Molecular Weight	799.8 g/mol	696.7 g/mol	327.34 g/mol

DIFFUSION AND OSMOSIS WORKSHEET

C H A P T E R 6

Name _____

Section _____

Date _____

Answer all questions on a *separate sheet* of paper.

Complete Data Table 6.1 below and use your data to answer questions 1–4:

Data Table 6.1. Results from the Osmosis and Diffusion Experiment

	Inside Start	Inside End	Outside Start	Outside End
Cl^-				
SO_4^{2-}				
Starch				
BSA (protein)				
Weight of bag (g)				

1. Which ions were able to move through the dialysis tubing? Which direction did they move? Why did the ions move in this direction?

2. Were starch and protein able to move through the dialysis membrane? Why or why not?

3. Did water move through the dialysis membrane? If so, in which direction? Why is this?

4. How would increasing the concentration of BSA in this experiment affect the results?

Diffusion in Gels

5. Which dye had the greatest rate of diffusion? What property of the dye determined the rate of diffusion?

6. Which plate had the greatest rates of diffusion, the one at room temperature or the one on ice? Why?

Elodea Plasmolysis

7. What happened to the *Elodea* cell when you added the 35% sucrose solution to the slide? Why?

8. What then happened when you added distilled water to the slide? Why did this occur?

Critical Thinking Questions (i.e., stuff you have to look up)

9. What organ in your body is responsible for maintaining proper osmoregularity? Think about this and explain why it is bad to drink ocean water.

10. Animal cells lack a cell wall—how do single-celled organisms keep from bursting when the osmotic conditions become hypotonic?

CELLULAR RESPIRATION

C H A P T E R   7

After completing this laboratory, you should be able to:

- Describe the major purposes of each stage in cellular respiration.

- Identify the stages of cellular respiration that produce CO_2, ethanol, and ATP.

- Understand the combined simple gas laws and be able to convert data to STP conditions.

- Describe the process of distillation and outline its uses in science and industry.

All life on earth performs a process known as **cellular respiration** to obtain energy from organic molecules. Cellular respiration is a complicated series of enzyme-catalyzed reactions ultimately releasing energy used by the cell for maintenance and growth.

This laboratory will focus upon one of the best understood cellular respiration pathways, the breakdown of the sugar glucose (Figure 7.1). All known organisms are capable of performing some, if not all, of the steps illustrated on the next page. Some organisms are only capable of performing cellular respiration with no oxygen present. These organisms are known as **obligate anaerobic organisms**. Obligate anaerobic organisms are always single-celled prokaryotes. Other organisms are capable of utilizing oxygen to further break down organic molecules. The more complete breakdown of these molecules in the presence of oxygen releases more energy per glucose molecule than an anaerobic pathway. **Obligate aerobic organisms** are organisms that must have oxygen present in order to survive. Humans are an example of these types of organisms (being without oxygen for just seven minutes can be fatal to humans). However, some organisms, such as yeast, may utilize aerobic respiration pathways when oxygen is present, but if oxygen is absent, they are capable of switching to

anaerobic respiration pathways. These organisms are known as **facultative anaerobic organisms**.

The first stage of both aerobic and anaerobic respiration pathways is **glycolysis**. Glycolysis is a ten-step process occurring in the cytoplasm. In glycolysis, glucose, a six-carbon molecule, is broken down to form two molecules of pyruvate, a three-carbon molecule. In the process, a net of two ATPs are formed and two NAD^+ are converted to NADH. NAD^+ is a coenzyme that is in limited supply in the cell. If all of the NAD^+ is converted to NADH, glycolysis stops. Therefore, there must be a mechanism to convert the NADH back to NAD^+ or no further cellular respiration can occur.

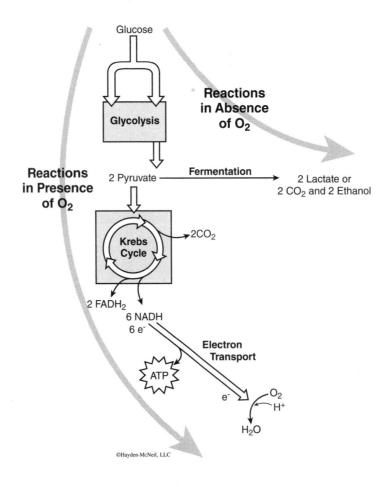

Figure 7.1. An Overview of Cellular Respiration

Ethanol and **lactic acid fermentation** are two mechanisms found in nature that organisms capable of living under anaerobic conditions have for converting NADH back to NAD$^+$. In ethanol fermentation, a molecule of pyruvate is converted to ethanol (C_2H_5OH) and CO_2. NADH is converted to NAD$^+$, but no ATP is formed. In lactic acid fermentation, a molecule of pyruvate is converted to lactic acid and NADH is converted to NAD$^+$. When mammalian muscles are strained and become starved for oxygen and NAD$^+$ (e.g., during vigorous exercise), they undergo lactic acid fermentation to replenish their NAD$^+$. There is no net energy gain as neither process produces ATP. The regenerated NAD$^+$ can now be used for glycolyis (Fig. 7.1).

Under aerobic conditions, however, aerobic organisms can further break down pyruvate and produce more ATP. **Aerobic respiration** typically consists of three steps: conversion of pyruvate to acetyl Co-A, the Krebs cycle, and electron transport phosphorylation (Figure 7.2). Conversion of a molecule of pyruvate to acetyl Co-A produces a molecule of CO_2 and converts a NAD$^+$ to NADH. The Krebs cycle produces two more ATPs and converts more NAD$^+$ to NADH. Further, another

coenzyme, FAD, is converted to FADH$_2$. However, the last step of respiration, the electron transport chain and oxidative phosphorylation, is the step that oxidizes the NADH and FADH$_2$ to regenerate NAD$^+$ and FAD. Electrons taken from NADH and FADH$_2$ pass down an electron transport chain, powering H$^+$ pumps along the inner mitochondrial membrane. The ultimate acceptor of the electrons freed from NADH and FADH$_2$ is oxygen—the oxygen combines with H$^+$ and the electrons to form water. The built up concentration of H$^+$ in the inter-membrane space serves as a potential energy source, which, when released, fuels ATP synthases that convert ADP to ATP. When everything is all said and done, aerobic respiration can produce from 34 to 36 molecules of ATP per molecule of glucose.

Respiration in Yeast

Yeast are single-celled fungi that are facultative anaerobes—they are capable of performing both aerobic and anaerobic respiration. Your instructor has prepared several aerobic and anaerobic yeast cultures for your study. Your goal will be to test for the production of CO_2 and ethanol in the yeast cultures under aerobic and anaerobic conditions.

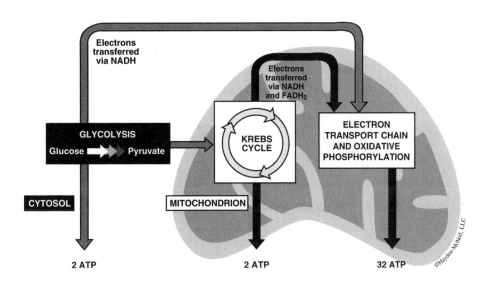

Figure 7.2. Aerobic Respiration

DO YEAST PRODUCE CO₂ UNDER AEROBIC AND ANAEROBIC CONDITIONS?

This demonstration will test for the presence of CO_2 in the gaseous efflux of yeast cultured under aerobic and anaerobic conditions. The gaseous efflux from these cultures will be passed through a solution of $Ba(OH)_2$. $Ba(OH)_2$ will react with any CO_2, producing $BaCO_3$, which is insoluble and will settle out as a white precipitate.

Your TA will set up the demonstration. Two Erlenmeyer flasks are set up on the bench, one containing an aerobic and one containing an anaerobic yeast culture. The Erlenmeyer flasks contain a rubber stopper on top with an output for any gaseous efflux. Your TA will place each of the gaseous efflux outputs in test tubes containing $Ba(OH)_2$. Be sure to note that the $Ba(OH)_2$ solution was initially colorless. After about thirty minutes, check the $Ba(OH)_2$ solutions; if they are white, indicating the presence of $BaCO_3$, then CO_2 is produced by the yeast culture.

Please note that the air feeding into the aerobic culture does not contain any CO_2—any $BaCO_3$ produced by the aerobic culture is entirely due to the production of CO_2 by the yeast.

RESPIRATION IN YEAST: DO YEAST PRODUCE ETHANOL UNDER AEROBIC AND ANAEROBIC CONDITIONS?

This experiment will test for the presence of ethanol in the solution of yeast cultured under aerobic and anaerobic conditions. This is done by heating the yeast culture and then distilling the vapors.

Distillation is a process of separating solutions by adding and then removing heat. Distillation is based on the fact that the vapor of a boiling mixture at lower heat levels will be richer in the components that have lower boiling points. In this case, ethanol has a boiling point of 78°C and water has a boiling point of 100°C. Ethanol distillation is commonly used in industry to prepare alcoholic beverages stronger than beer and wine. Alcohol is a poison, and when the alcohol concentration in a culture reaches about 15%, it will kill the yeast. To further concentrate the alcohol, one must distill it.

Your instructor has prepared two stills (Figure 7.3), one containing an aerobic culture and one containing an anaerobic culture. First, the two culture mixtures are heated to a point above the boiling point of ethanol but below the boiling point of water

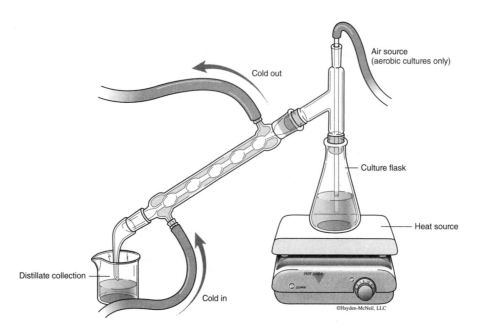

Figure 7.3. Distillation of Aerobic and Anaerobic Yeast Cultures

(about 85°C in this case). This initially separates the ethanol from the water as the majority (but not all!) of the vapor will be ethanol. The gas then passes through the condenser. The condenser is a tube with numerous traps surrounded by a current of cold water. The water cools the vapors, causing them to condense in the traps. The higher the boiling point, the quicker the condenser will cause the gas to condense. In this example, water will condense in the first traps while the ethanol will be able to pass farther down the condenser. Eventually, an enriched solution of ethanol will drip from the condenser into the collection beaker.

PROCEDURE

Prepare four solutions as indicated in the chart below.

Be sure you are wearing protective eyewear while preparing the four tubes below. NaOH and the strong I_2KI solutions are very caustic and can cause eye damage. Also, be sure that you are using the appropriate color-coded pipette for each chemical to prevent contamination. If you have laboratory in the early morning, you may have to wait until the end of laboratory for the still to produce enough distillate to perform the experiment. When the four tubes are prepared, place a square of Parafilm over each, shake vigorously, and let stand for five to ten minutes. If ethanol is present, it will react with iodine in the presence of a strong base and form **iodoform**, which will settle out as a yellow precipitate.

Tube 1 is the negative control. This control will ensure that there is no ethanol contaminating the water supply used to prepare the cultures. Tube 2 is the positive control. Since we know ethanol is present in Tube 2, we expect iodoform to form. If it does, we can be confident that our chemicals were prepared properly. If no precipitate forms in Tube 2, add an additional 1.0 ml of I_2KI to *each* tube, shake, and let sit for another five minutes. If no precipitate forms after this second addition of I_2KI, tell your instructor.

Tubes 3 and 4 are the experimental tubes. Carefully observe each tube for the presence of the yellow precipitate iodoform. If present, then that serves as an indicator for alcohol; if not, then one can conclude that there is no ethanol present. Record all data in Data Table 7.2.

Aerobic Respiration in Lentils

If aerobic organisms are placed in a closed system, they will consume oxygen and produce carbon dioxide in a roughly 1:1 basis. Therefore, the total amount of gaseous molecules in the system will not change. However, if carbon dioxide is chemically removed from the system as it is formed, the pressure of the system will drop as oxygen is consumed. Oxygen consumed is not replaced by carbon dioxide because the carbon dioxide is being removed from the gaseous state.

In a closed system changes in pressure and volume are related by what is known in physics as the *Combined Simple Gas Laws*:

$$\frac{PV}{T} = K \qquad \text{Where K is a constant}$$

Table 7.1. Preparation of Experimental Flasks for the Determination of Ethanol in Aerobic and Anaerobic Yeast Cultures

	Water	95% Ethanol	I_2KI	NaOH	Distillate
Tube 1—negative control	2.5 ml	—	1.0 ml	1.5 ml	—
Tube 2—positive control	1.25 ml	1.25 ml	1.0 ml	1.5 ml	—
Tube 3—aerobic culture	—	—	1.0 ml	1.5 ml	2.5 ml
Tube 4—anaerobic culture	—	—	1.0 ml	1.5 ml	2.5 ml

If the system remains closed throughout the experiment, any changes in pressure, volume, or temperature will be related as indicated in the formula below:

$$\frac{P_1 V_1}{T_1} = \frac{P_2 V_2}{T_2}$$

We will be utilizing this relationship when we convert our results to standard temperature and pressure later in this experiment.

For this experiment, we will construct a simple pressure and volume measurement device as figured below (Figure 7.4). First, measure out approximately 12 g of lentils and record the weight of the lentils used. It is not critical that you get exactly 12.0 g, but an amount close to 12 g is good enough. However, it is critical that the actual weight of the lentils is accurately weighed and recorded. Place the lentils in the reaction tube. Next, obtain a wad of non-absorbent cotton, about the size of a cotton ball, and place the cotton in the tube on top of the lentils. Make sure that the cotton is about 2 cm thick. The cotton is present to protect the lentils from being damaged by the KOH. Too little cotton will not protect the lentils from damage while too much will slow down the removal of CO_2 from the system. Avoid compressing the cotton too much as this also interferes with gas exchange in the system. Finally, carefully spoon in about 1.5 cm of KOH pellets into the tube. Be sure you close the lid on the KOH container when you are done as KOH is highly ascorbic and water from the air will cause the KOH to go into solution.

Carefully place the rubber stopper on the tube. The rubber stopper may have sharp edges protruding from the bottom so be sure you do not stick yourself. Attach a 1.0 ml pipette to the rubber tubing point-side in. This will ensure that as the pressure drops, the measurements will be from 0.0 to 1.0 ml. Adjust the plunger on the syringe so that it is about half way out. Finally, fill the dropper of methyl blue and place at the end of the pipette. Carefully squeeze the dropper and slowly pull up on the syringe plunger. This will pull a bead of methyl blue into the pipette.

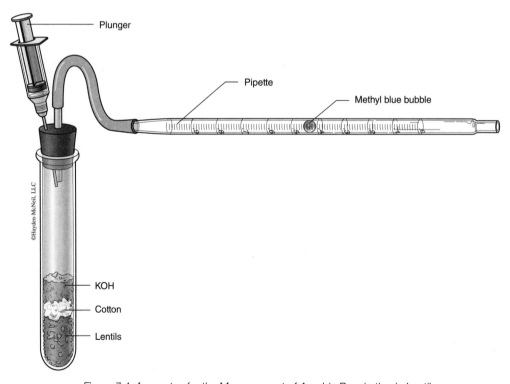

Plunger

Pipette

Methyl blue bubble

©Hayden-McNeil, LLC

KOH

Cotton

Lentils

Figure 7.4. Apparatus for the Measurement of Aerobic Respiration in Lentils

Slowly pull up and push down the plunger so that the methyl blue coats the inner surface of the pipette. This will reduce surface tension inside the pipette and allow for more accurate measurements.

Let the system set for ten minutes. During this time, the KOH will be removing the ambient CO_2 from the system. Be sure to watch the bead of methyl blue during this time—if it comes close to the end of the pipette, slowly adjust the syringe plunger to push the bead back out.

After ten minutes, adjust the plunger to 0.0 ml and start timing. Every three minutes for a total of 15 minutes, record the volume of oxygen consumption, indicated by the methyl blue bead, in Data Table 7.3. When you are completed, carefully take the system apart. Rinse out the pipette, being careful because methyl blue will permanently stain clothing. Discard the KOH in the appropriate container on the center bench. *Do not* throw KOH away in the trash! Use the long tweezers to remove the cotton and lentils. You may throw these away. Do not discard them in the KOH waste receptacle.

For this experiment, two types of lentils will be used, "normal" and "freeze-thawed" lentils. Normal lentils are healthy lentils, which have been activated by placing them in water. Freeze-thawed lentils were placed in a freezer at $-20°C$ and then thawed. When frozen, water inside the mitochondria expanded, causing them to rupture when thawed. This will damage the mitochondria and inhibit their ability to perform aerobic respiration by not allowing the mitochondria to build up a concentration of H^+. Another feature of this experiment will be to measure the degree to which freeze-thawing will affect the lentil's ability to perform aerobic respiration.

Make sure you record the room temperature and pressure. These will be used later on in your analysis of the data.

DATA ANALYSIS

Plot the data from both the normal and freeze-thawed data sets by placing the time on the x-axis and the volume of oxygen consumed on the y-axis. Information on how to create graphs is given in Appendix A. Generate the slope for each line. The slope is a measure of the respiration rate of each set of lentils.

Now divide the reaction rate of each set of lentils by the weight. This will give you a corrected measure of volume of oxygen consumed per minute per gram of lentils. If more lentils were used, they would obviously consume more oxygen. Corrections such as this make the respiration rate relevant to any size sample.

The final correction that must be made to the data is to convert the reaction rates to **standard temperature and pressure (STP)**. By convention, standard temperature is defined as 0°C (273 K) and standard pressure is 1 atm (760 mmHg). Had you performed this experiment under different environmental conditions, like a warmer room temperature or under lower pressure, the results would have been slightly different. To make data readily comparable between researchers working under different environmental conditions, it was agreed upon to always present data converted to STP conditions. To do so, use the combined simple gas laws presented earlier. The conditions for T_1 and P_1 are the room temperature and pressure, respectively. Note that for this equation to work, all temperatures must be converted to the Kelvin absolute temperature scale (K = °C + 273). The value of V_1 is the corrected rate of oxygen consumption. One can use this because the unit of this rate is ml/min*g. The numerator is a unit of volume. Since the units in the denominator, time and weight, don't change when pressure or temperature are changed, they will not affect our calculations.

The conditions on the other side of the equation are those indicated for STP, P_2 = 760 mmHg and T_2 = 273 K. Solving the equation for V_2, the corrected respiration rate at STP, you will get:

$$V_2 = \frac{P_1 V_1 T_2}{T_1 P_2}$$

Solving for V_2 will give you the corrected respiration rate under STP conditions.

Once you have the rates for both the normal lentils and the freeze-thawed lentils converted to STP, use the formula below to calculate the percent inhibition that freeze-thawing had on the lentil's ability to perform aerobic respiration:

$$\%I = \frac{R_N - R_{FT}}{R_N}$$

Where

    $\%I$ = Percent Inhibition

    R_N = Respiration rate of normal lentils

    R_{FT} = Respiration rate of freeze-thawed lentils

MITOSIS AND MEIOSIS

CHAPTER 8

After completing this laboratory, you should be able to:

- Understand the genetic significance of mitosis and meiosis.

- Identify and describe the stages of mitosis and meiosis in both plant and animal cells.

- Recreate the events of mitosis and meiosis using models.

- Describe the events of crossing-over and the ramifications of this event on gamete formation.

- Discuss the advantages and disadvantages of sexual and asexual reproduction.

Mitosis is the process through which a cell (called the **mother cell**) divides, forming two **daughter cells** that are genetically identical to each other *and* to the mother cell. It was first observed under a microscope in the 1880s and most of the terminology associated with mitosis is in reference to features easily observed under a microscope. As our knowledge became more complete, some of these terms were modified to include processes that occur at a molecular level and remain unseen under a light microscope.

The cycle of a cell is called the **cell cycle** (Figure 8.1). The cell cycle consists of five stages: **interphase, prophase, metaphase, anaphase,** and **telophase** (Figure 8.2). A cell that is not undergoing mitosis is said to be in Interphase. Modern cytologists, however, have more finely tuned the cell cycle. Interphase is now broken down into three substages, the G_1, **S,** and G_2 stage (Interphase = G_1 + S + G_2). Most of the growth and cellular functions of a cell occur during the G_1 and G_2 stages while the DNA is replicated during the S stage. Each chromosome is exactly duplicated—later on, when the chromosomes become visible, the two identical chromosomal units are known as **sister chromatids.**

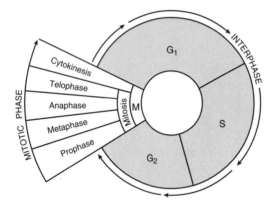

Figure 8.1. The Cell Cycle

When mitosis begins, the cell enters prophase. Prophase is the longest phase of mitosis and is sometimes broken down into three substages: early prophase, middle prophase, and late prophase. During early prophase, the chromosomes appear to be less homogenous and the nucleoli disappear. Centrioles begin moving toward the pole and the spindle fiber formation begins. During middle prophase the chromosomes become visible but are all mixed together (it looks like a big plate of spaghetti). The nuclear membrane begins to dissolve. In late prophase, the chromosomes have fully condensed and are visible as distinct units. In some literature, middle and late prophase are combined and called **prometaphase.**

During metaphase, the chromosomes line up in the middle of the cell, an area called the **metaphase plate.** If you play with the focus and contrast, you

can see the spindle fibers attaching to a special area of the centromeres of each chromosome known as the **kinetochore.** During **anaphase,** the motor proteins of the kinetochore region of the centromere activate, break the centromere, which separates the sister chromatids. Motor proteins on each chromosome then cause them to "walk" down the spindle fiber toward each pole. When the chromosomes arrive at the poles, we say that the cell is in telophase. The nuclear membrane will reform and the chromosomes will start to become diffuse. It is during **telophase** that the bulk of **cytokinesis** occurs. Cytokinesis is a process independent of mitosis that separates the mother cell into two daughter cells.

Mitosis in Animal Cells—The Whitefish Blastula

A **blastula** is a stage in the early development of an organism. Essentially, a blastula is a ball of rapidly-dividing, undifferentiated cells, making it ideal for studying mitosis. Obtain a whitefish blastula slide and observe under the scanning (4×) objective lens. The large reddish balls you see are the blastulae, not individual cells. Focus on one blastula and increase magnification. Under higher power, you should be able to see the nuclear regions of the cells. The nucleus is not very distinct in interphase cells—use this as your identifying feature for interphase cells. The nucleus is still there, it just doesn't stain well using the preparation techniques used to stain the chromosomes. The mitotic stages should be readily apparent based upon chromosome arrangement.

Observe and draw a cell in each stage of the cell cycle. You do not need to draw separate early, middle, and late prophase, but see if you can find each of them.

Mitosis in Plant Cells—The Onion Root Tip

The growing tips of roots contain meristematic regions. Like the whitefish blastulae, the meristematic region of roots contains rapidly dividing, undifferentiated cells. Additionally, the cell walls of plant cells make the cellular boundaries much more distinct and observations even easier. Observe the growing root tip of onion (*Allium*) under the

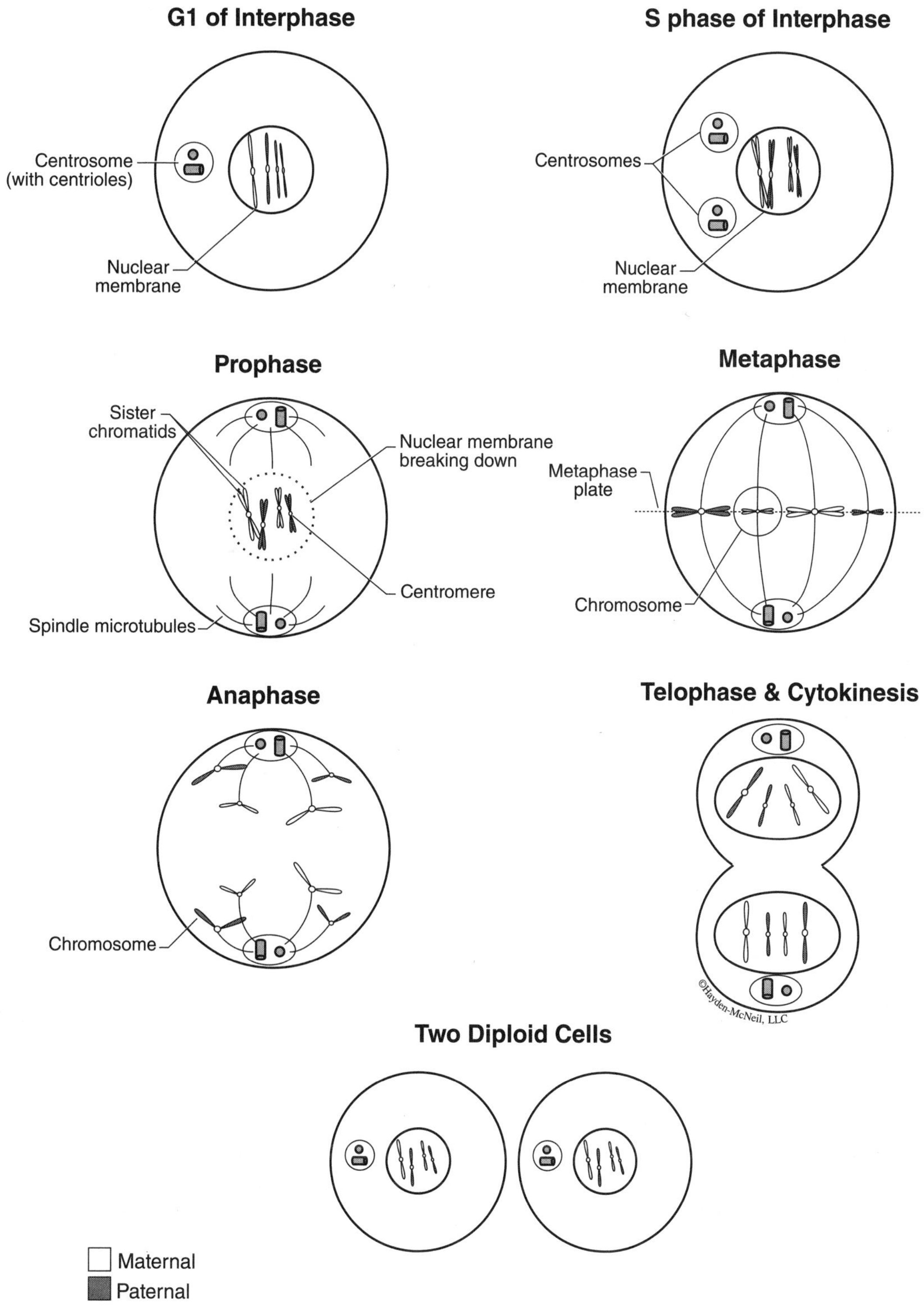

G1 of Interphase

Centrosome
(with centrioles)

Nuclear
membrane

S phase of Interphase

Centrosomes

Nuclear
membrane

Prophase

Sister
chromatids

Nuclear membrane
breaking down

Centromere

Spindle microtubules

Metaphase

Metaphase
plate

Chromosome

Anaphase

Chromosome

Telophase & Cytokinesis

©Hayden-McNeil, LLC

Two Diploid Cells

☐ Maternal
■ Paternal

Figure 8.2. An Overview of Mitosis

scanning objective. You will want to concentrate on the region just above the root tip. This is known as the zone of cell division and will contain the most cells undergoing mitosis.

The nucleus in cells in interphase will look like solid circles. As the chromosomes become visible, the other stages should be easily seen. During late telophase, cytokinesis has almost come to completion and the chromosomes have started to become more diffuse—if you see two small adjacent cells that look like they are in prophase, it is probably two cells in telophase. Observe and draw a cell in each stage of the cell cycle.

Mitosis Exercise—Using Chromosome Models to Understand Mitosis

You should have a set of yellow and red beads as well as some magnetized white plastic tubes with pink and blue tape at your lab station. We will be using these simple tools to model the events of mitosis. The beads represent gene loci. The different colors of the bands represent different alleles. The gene loci are strung together like pearls on a necklace, very similar to our own chromosomes. The magnetized white plastic tubes represent the centromeres. Since the organism we are representing is diploid, it received one half of its chromosomes from the sperm and one half from the egg. For each chromosome pair, one centromere will be blue (representing the genetic contribution of the sperm) and one chromosome will be pink (representing the genetic contribution of the egg).

To start, use the beads and construct the chromosomes of a 2N = 4 organism as illustrated below. We are using a 2N = 4 organism because this will allow you to demonstrate your knowledge of mitosis while not getting bogged down with the total number of chromosomes (if these were human chromosomes, there would be 23 pairs, each with about 1500 beads).

The first thing that must occur is the DNA needs to replicate. This actually occurs during the S stage of the cell cycle, long before mitosis begins. Replicate each chromosome by taking appropriate colored centromeres and creating new chromosomes with the alleles (beads) in exactly the same sequence. The two replicates are joined (via the magnets inside) to form two **sister chromatids**.

During prophase, the chromosomes will become visible. Next, during metaphase, the four pairs of sister chromatids will line up in the middle of the cell.

During anaphase, the centromeres will break, separating each sister chromatid from its replicate. The spindle fibers will contract, pulling one identical sister chromatid to each of the two poles. During telophase, the nuclear membrane will reform and cytokinesis will take place, creating two identical daughter cells.

Are the chromosomes in each daughter cell genetically unique or genetically identical? What is the significance of this phenomenon? A summary of mitosis is given in Figure 8.2.

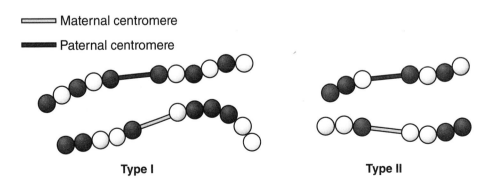

Maternal centromere

Paternal centromere

Type I   **Type II**

Figure 8.3. 2N = 4 Chromosomes for Mitosis and Meiosis Exercise

Meiosis
INTRODUCTION

Nearly every organism has the capability to exchange genes at some point in its life cycle. Sexual reproduction produces the genetic variability organisms need to adapt and evolve to the ever-changing environment. The ability to exchange genes is known as sexuality. Sex, however, is not synonymous with reproduction. Sexuality refers to the ability to exchange genes with another organism. Reproduction refers to the ability to increase the number of individuals in a population. Some organisms, like the *Paramecium* you observed in the cells lab, can swap genes (sexuality) without increasing in number (no reproduction).

Not all organisms reproduce sexually, and those that reproduce sexually do not necessarily reproduce sexually every generation. Many organisms, such as aphids and plants, intersperse generations of sexual reproduction among generations of asexual reproduction. Many simpler organisms, such as bacteria, exchange genetic information without meiosis or recombination. These organisms exchange tiny pieces of DNA on specialized structures called **plasmids**. They can also pick loose pieces of DNA directly from the environment. This process is called **bacterial transformation.**

Humans are diploid; we use instructions from two sets of chromosomes. By combining genetic material from both of our parents, we are a synthesis of information from two different individuals, creating a genetically unique offspring. To have offspring of our own, there must be a way of producing cells with single sets of chromosomes. These haploid cells can then be recombined with another set of haploid cells, recreating a diploid organism.

Meiosis is a sequence of two nuclear and cytoplasmic divisions that ultimately halve the number of chromosomes in each of the four daughter cells. In animals, these haploid daughter cells will mature to form **gametes** (Figure 8.3). Plants have a much more complicated process through which gametes are produced. This will be discussed in greater detail in Chapter 13, Plant Reproduction and Diversity.

During sexual reproduction, the fusion of two compatible gametes results in a diploid nucleus called a **zygote**. The diploid zygote nucleus has two complete sets of homologous chromosomes.

The diploid offspring produced by sexual reproduction are never genetically identical to either of their parents. This is the result of the recombination between homologous chromosomes and independent assortment of each chromosome in the homologous pair.

Recombination is the mixing and matching of alleles from homologous chromosomes. Note that for diploid eukaryotic organisms, recombination has a different meaning than in prokaryotes. Eukaryotic recombination takes place during prophase I of meiosis via the process of **crossing-over** (Figure 8.5). During crossing-over, fragments from one homolog will break off and be swapped with an equal sized piece from another homolog. Crossing-over can only ever occur between homologs and only exchange pieces of equal size. If either of these conditions is not met, then a chromosomal mutation will occur.

Independent assortment is the random migration of different members of each chromosome pair to different poles of the cell. When you produce sex cells, the chromosomes that ultimately came from your father do not stay together, they mingle at random with the chromosomes that came from your mother.

Meiosis evolved from mitosis, so the stages are very similar looking under the microscope. However, there are some subtle yet profound differences. First of all, there are two stages of meiosis, cleverly named meiosis I and meiosis II. Each stage of meiosis consists of a prophase, metaphase, anaphase, and a telophase. Additionally, before meiosis takes place, the chromosomes replicate, creating two identical sister chromatids. You may ask yourself why, if we are ultimately trying to reduce the number of chromosomes, the first thing we do is replicate them? There is no easy answer to this—evolution does not always occur in a logical manner. What we do know

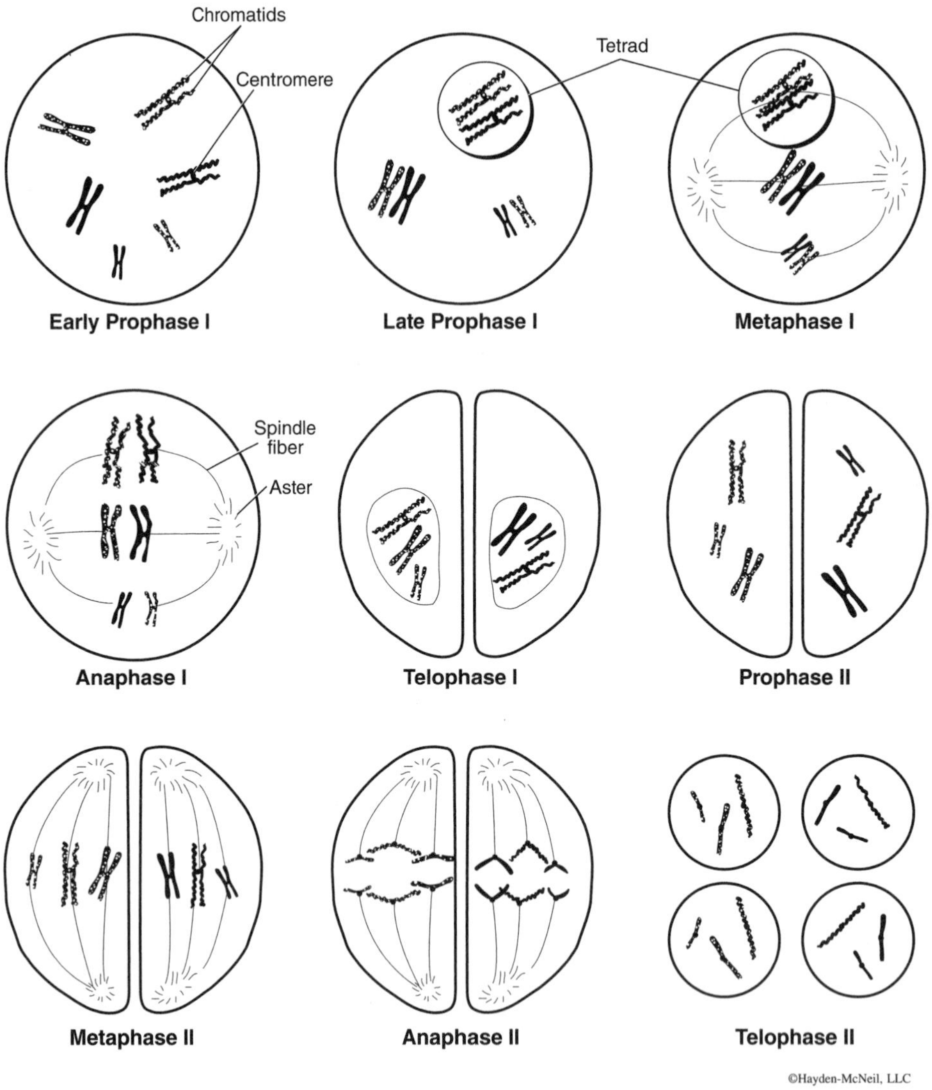

Figure 8.4. An Overview of Meiosis

is that the chromosomes do replicate and meiosis proceeds from there.

Most of the significant events leading to the formation of genetically unique haploid gametes occur during prophase I, so we will spend some time looking at this. First, the chromosomes have already replicated. However, unlike mitosis, the two pairs of homologs come together, forming a four-chromatid structure known as a **tetrad**. While in the tetrad stage of prophase I, crossing-over takes place.

Pieces from one homolog will be exchanged with equivalent pieces from another homolog.

During metaphase I, the tetrads will line up along the metaphase plate. However, how they line up is randomly determined—there is a 50% chance that either the maternal or the paternal homologs will be facing a given pole. Are there any other possible orientations of the tetrads, other than the ones you have illustrated?

Meiosis I Permits Crossing-Over and Genetic <u>Recombination</u>

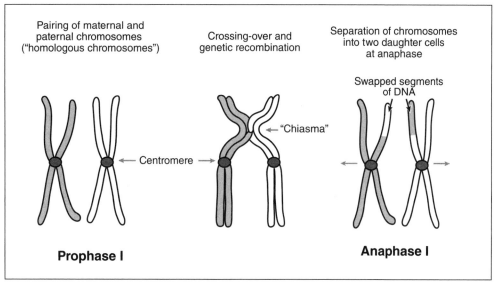

Note: Only **one** cross-over event is shown. It is possible, however, for a number of cross-overs and recombinations to occur.
Only **nonsister** chromatids cross over and recombine. Different versions (alleles) of a gene are then combined with other genes.

Figure 8.5. Crossing-Over During Prophase I

During anaphase I, the spindle fibers will shorten, breaking the tetrad and separating the maternal and paternal centromeres (i.e., with your models, the two pinks will go to one side and the two blues will go to the other—you cannot have one pink and one blue go to one side and one pink and one blue go to the other). During telophase I, the nuclear membrane will reform and cytokinesis will take place, creating two daughter cells.

Meiosis II is very similar to mitosis—there is no crossing-over. During prophase II, the chromosomes condense and the nuclear membrane disolves During metaphase II, the chromosomes of each daughter cell line up in their respective metaphase plates. During anaphase II, the spindle fibers shorten and the sister chromatids separate. During telophase II, the nuclear membrane reforms and cytokinesis takes place, creating four genetically unique daughter cells. Are any of the resulting gametes identical?

Now take one of your four gametes and "mate" it with a randomly selected gamete from another group. Look around the classroom—were any of the resulting zygotes identical to yours? Remember that this exercise was only done with a 2N = 4 organism with very short chromosomes—in your cells, you would have 2N = 46 chromosomes, each over 1500 beads long! A comparison of mitosis and meiosis is given in Figure 8.6.

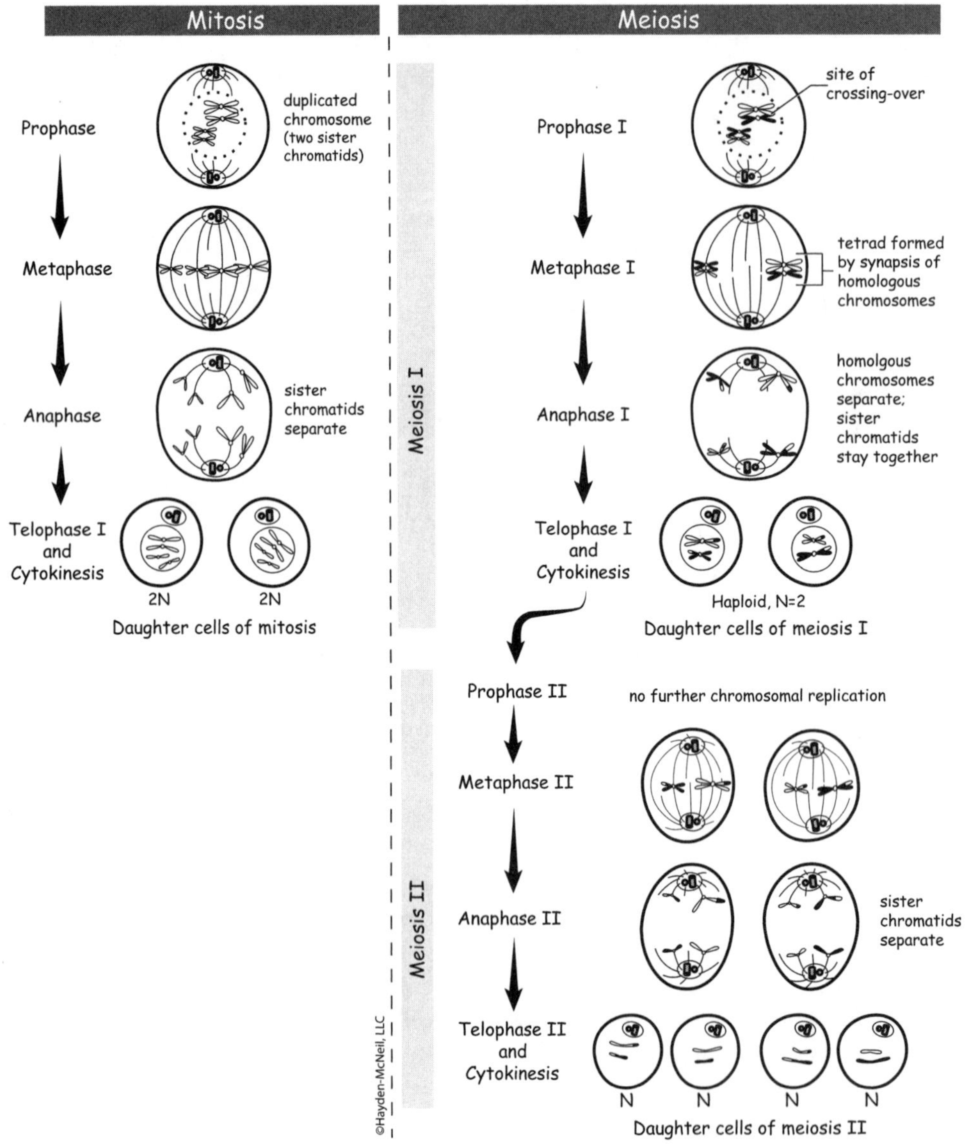

Figure 8.6. A Comparison between Mitosis and Meiosis in 2N = 4 Cells

PATERNITY DETERMINATION IN WHOOPING CRANES

CHAPTER 9

The gels you will be using contain *Ethidium Bromide*. This chemical is a known mutagen and a carcinogen. The amount used in this lab is extremely small. There is no real danger to you if you follow the instructions closely. As a precaution, be sure to wear gloves at all times during this lab.

NO FOOD OR DRINK IN THE LAB
THIS WEEK

After completing this laboratory, you should be able to:

* Describe the ecologic and genetic plight of the whooping crane.

* Understand the theory behind gel electrophoresis, PCR, and STR analysis.

* Perform gel electrophoresis and interpret the results.

The Whooping Crane

The adult whooping crane *(Grus americana)* is pure white in color with black wingtips, black legs and feet, black facial markings, and has a bare patch of red skin on its head. First-year chicks also have black wingtips, but their body feathers are tawny brown and white. Standing up to 5 feet tall with a 7 to 8 foot wingspan, the whooping crane is the tallest bird in North America. Males average 16 pounds and females 14 pounds.

The whooper's name was inspired by its loud, distinctive call, audible up to two miles away! This breathtaking bugle is created by resonance in the bird's 5-foot-long trachea (half of which is looped within the keel of the breastbone). Cranes call to communicate danger, to defend territory, and to reinforce pair bonds.

The History of the Whooping Crane

The whooping crane is one of the most endangered birds in the world today. The current (2007) wild population is about 320 individuals. The migratory whoopers are divided into three populations: the 230-bird Aransas (Texas)–Wood Buffalo National Park (Canada) population, a non-migratory flock in Florida consisting of 40 birds, and a new (introduced in 2002) migratory flock in Florida–Wisconsin of 50 birds. Although the wild population is not increasing dramatically, the numbers are not going down. The establishment of the new migratory flock will ensure that one major disaster, such as a hurricane, will not destroy the entire wild population.

The whooping crane is endangered today because of the encroachment of civilization into their habitat. As the western United States was settled, their population, which was estimated to be 1300 in 1865, began to decline. Whoopers need grasslands and wetlands to survive and reproduce, and both were destroyed as the farming began. By 1938, only 22 whooping cranes remained.

Before wildlife biologists could help restore the whooping crane, they needed to find the nesting grounds. In 1955, a fire crew found the cranes nesting in Wood Buffalo National Park in Canada's

Northwest Territories. Biologists in Canada and the U.S. worked together to develop a plan and in 1967, one egg from each of six two-egg clutches was transferred from Wood Buffalo Park to the Patuxent Wildlife Research Center in Laurel, Maryland. Over the next six years 44 more eggs were removed and hatched in the US. Because whoopers do not reach breeding age until they are between 5 and 10 years old, the captive female whoopers could not be bred until 1975.

During the next 13 years, the captive whooper population at Patuxent grew to a healthy 58. With all the birds at a single location, the possibility of a single disaster, like a disease outbreak, was a constant fear. It was decided in late 1989 that the captive flock be split and that the second location should be the International Crane Foundation in Baraboo, Wisconsin. Twenty-two whooping cranes went to Baraboo in a military plane and were welcomed by 400 local school children. The ICF now houses 35 whoopers and has shipped birds to the Calgary Zoo, the San Antonio Zoo, and to release programs.

Whooping Crane Paternity Cases

Experience has shown that whooping cranes do not breed successfully in captivity. Scientists are unsure as to whether this is due to a behavioral change when living in captivity, the lack of an environmental cue, or some completely unknown factor. In any case, scientists have taken to artificially inseminating whooping crane eggs to increase the whooping crane flocks. Results from the initial attempts using the semen from one male were not good. Later experiments showed that an acceptable rate of egg fertility could be obtained by artificially inseminating the eggs with a mixture of semen from many potential fathers. This, however, presents one small problem: if a mixture of semen from different potential fathers is used, just who is the real father?

Determining parentage and relatedness is especially important in whooping crane population management because of the genetic bottleneck they went through in 1938. It is estimated that out of the 22 birds in 1938, only six to eight were mating pairs, leading scientists to hypothesize that the 300 birds alive today are not very genetically diverse. Genetic diversity is important because it keeps the population healthy. In a large population, several variations of a gene are represented, especially the genes that make a healthy individual. Undesirable genes such as those that cause disease or birth defects are present too, but natural selection culls them over generations, and ultimately allows the desirable genes to dominate. If, however, most of the gene pool is lost with a dwindling population, a disproportionate number of undesirable genes may prevail. In a small population, individuals with these undesirable genes have a chance to mate, allowing them to pass on undesirable traits.

Another problem with a small population is the higher incidence of inbreeding. If a population has a high incidence of inbreeding, there is a higher chance of hidden maladaptive (bad) genes being expressed. As a result of low genetic diversity and inbreeding because of the bottleneck, whooping cranes have a high incidence of scoliosis and spinal deformities when compared with other crane species. The whoopers also have low adaptability, meaning that they are very sensitive to changes in diet, or habitat and they exhibit a much lower resistance to exotic diseases. In other words, they have problems adapting to anything new. However, they do not exhibit other effects of inbreeding such as low fertility or low hatchability. So far, the whoopers have been lucky, and there have been no major problems. Only time will tell, however, as the effects of inbreeding sometimes occur after several generations. Whooping crane paternity cases are a historical problem. In the early days of the captive breeding program, the ICF did not have very many captive cranes to work with, and they had not perfected their artificial insemination techniques. Often the female crane was artificially inseminated with the semen of two or three males and, even with close record keeping, paternity was questionable. It is important to establish paternity so that inbreeding can be avoided. Using DNA profiling techniques, such as Short Tandem Repeat (STR) analysis, paternity can be determined in every case.

DNA Profiling

DNA profiling is defined as the analysis of DNA from one individual by molecular techniques to create a unique DNA profile. Traditional DNA profiling employed the technique of Southern Blotting using radioactive probes. Advances in DNA technology have made analysis by PCR a much more attractive method of DNA fingerprinting.

Source of DNA

The DNA used in determining whooping crane paternity cases is isolated from blood samples which are collected during yearly health checks of the birds. The DNA is purified from whole blood by lysing the blood cells and removing the other cellular components. An interesting fact is that unlike humans, birds possess nucleated red blood cells. Therefore, a very large amount of DNA can be obtained from a small amount of blood. This is not important in STR analysis because, as you will see, the amount of DNA of interest will be increased greatly (amplified) through the use of a process known as Polymerase Chain Reaction (PCR). By using PCR, even trace amounts of DNA can be amplified and used in molecular biology.

What Is PCR?

PCR stands for polymerase chain reaction (Figure 9.1). It is an in vitro method for copying specific pieces of DNA based on the process of DNA replication. The components required to synthesize DNA are:

- dNTPs (deoxynucleotide triphosphates)—the nucleotide building blocks of DNA

- bDNA—used as a template from which to synthesize the new strand of DNA

- DNA polymerase—the enzyme that carries out DNA synthesis

- magnesium ions—a cofactor required by the enzyme for its function

PCR employs a variation on this process using subsequent cycles of denaturation, primer annealing, and extension with DNA polymerase to copy (amplify) a target DNA sequence millions of times.

The main difference is the DNA polymerase used. PCR uses a heat-stable DNA polymerase, meaning it can withstand high temperatures without denaturing. This heat-stable DNA polymerase is found in thermophilic (heat-loving) bacteria. The first thermostable DNA polymerase was isolated from the bacterium *Thermus aquaticus* found living in hot springs in Yellowstone National Park and goes by the name Taq polymerase. This factor enables the temperature cycling. If a normal DNA polymerase were used, say from *E. coli*, which grows best at 37°C, fresh enzyme would need to be added after each denaturation step.

PCR uses a DNA primer to provide a starting point for the polymerase. This primer is a short piece of single-stranded DNA that is synthesized to be complementary to the sequence that borders, or flanks, the DNA to be amplified. Two primers are required for amplification, one for each DNA strand. These primers are incorporated into the final double-stranded PCR product. The steps of PCR are as follows:

- **Denaturation**—The reaction mix is heated to a high temperature (~94°C) to separate, or denature, the DNA strands. Double-stranded DNA is held together by hydrogen bonds, which are broken apart when heated.

- **Primer Annealing**—The reaction mix is cooled to a temperature ranging from 40°C to 72°C, at which the primers bind to their complementary strand of DNA. The actual temperature depends on the length and sequence of the primers used.

- **Primer Extension**—The reaction mix is heated to about 72°C, providing the optimal temperature for the Taq DNA polymerase to extend the primers by incorporating dNTPs complementary to the template strand.

The DNA synthesized during one cycle of PCR will serve as a template for each subsequent cycle. The result is a doubling of the target DNA present with each cycle. This exponential accumulation can produce millions of copies of the target DNA in about 20 cycles. It takes three cycles to produce the first discreet products. These are products that are bound on both sides by the primer, thus prohibiting extension past this point because there is no further DNA template.

Wildlife and Short Tandem Repeat (STR) Analysis

As our environment changes due to the human impact, wildlife will encounter challenges that will determine whether or not they will survive these changes. Genetic diversity in wildlife populations will aid the individuals as they encounter these challenges. Using Short Tandem Repeats (STRs) as their tool, wildlife biologists are investigating genetic diversity in current populations of several species including wolves, polar bears, and salmon. At Purdue University, genetic diversity in reintroduced elk populations in California and Pennsylvania has been studied using STRs. The scientists compared genetic diversity between the source populations and the new populations. The STR analysis showed very little genetic diversity in the reintroduced populations when compared to the source populations. In a sense, the introduced populations of elk went through a genetic bottleneck when only a few individuals from the source herd were used to create new populations. This new information will help wildlife managers reflect on how introduced populations will be maintained as well as how new populations will be managed.

In addition to studying wild animal populations, STRs can help captive populations (like the cranes) and help solve forensic cases that involve wildlife. When the San Diego Zoo acquired six confiscated endangered iguanas, they used STR analysis to determine if the six individuals were related. Using STRs they determined that the iguanas were siblings. STR profiles are routinely used in poaching cases to determine if meat or hides found at a perpetrator's residence match remains found on private or public property. In India, law enforcement uses STR profiles to determine if leopards, tigers, or lions are being poached for use in traditional medicine. Each big cat has a unique STR profile and confiscated tissue or body parts can be analyzed to determine which species it came from.

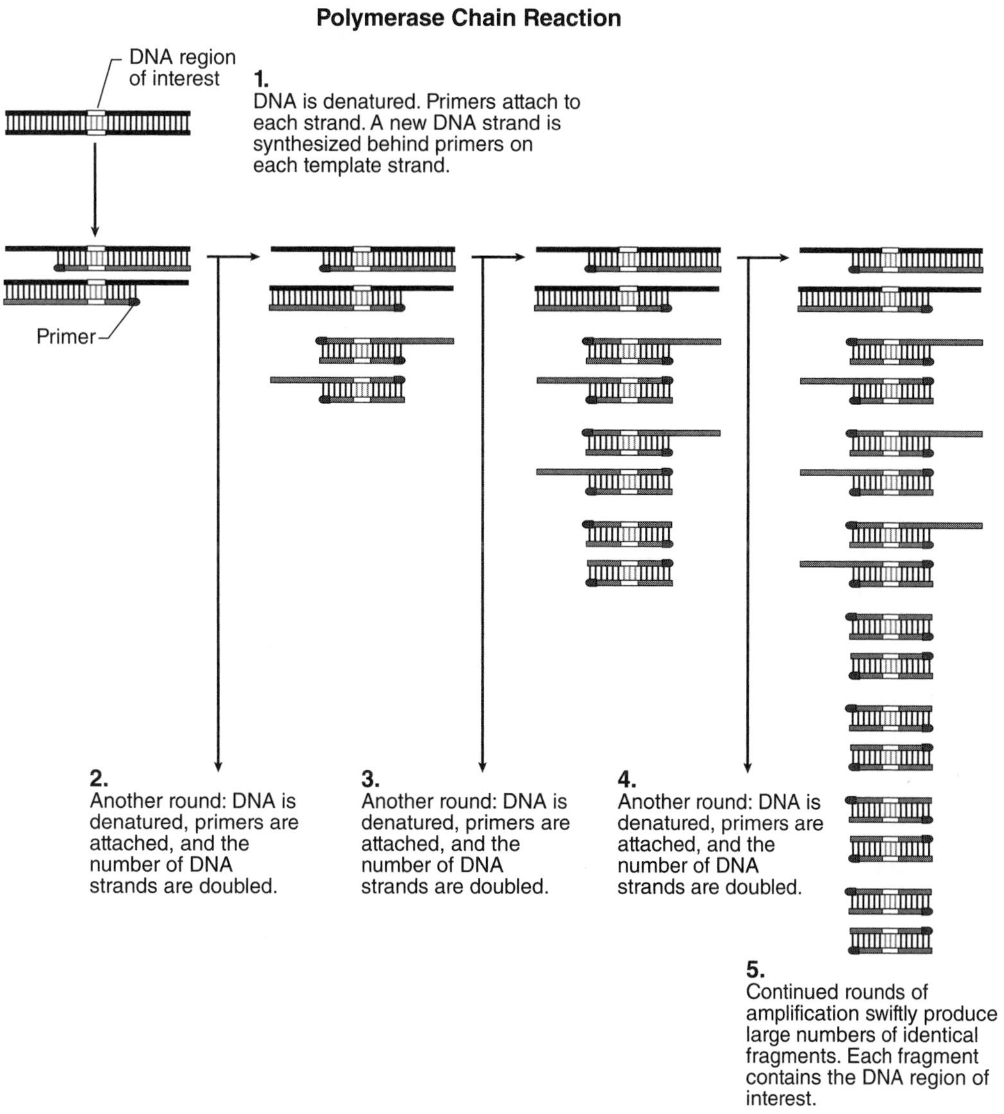

Polymerase Chain Reaction

DNA region of interest

1.
DNA is denatured. Primers attach to each strand. A new DNA strand is synthesized behind primers on each template strand.

Primer

2.
Another round: DNA is denatured, primers are attached, and the number of DNA strands are doubled.

3.
Another round: DNA is denatured, primers are attached, and the number of DNA strands are doubled.

4.
Another round: DNA is denatured, primers are attached, and the number of DNA strands are doubled.

5.
Continued rounds of amplification swiftly produce large numbers of identical fragments. Each fragment contains the DNA region of interest.

Figure 9.1. The Mechanism of Polymerase Chain Reaction

What Are Short Tandem Repeats (STRs)?

Short tandem repeats (STRs), also called microsatellites, are small genetic markers found in genomic DNA that consist of a two- to six-base-pair sequence that is repeated five to one hundred times. For example, the STR might be a stretch of DNA with the base pair sequence of CA repeated 25 times ($[CA]_{25}$) or AGG repeated five times ($[AGG]_5$) (Figure 9.2). They have been found in the genomes of mammals, birds, fish, insects, and some microorganisms. STRs are found throughout the genome in different unique loci, and they can have as many as 10 alleles or as few as one allele. A STR allele is simply the number of times the short DNA sequence is repeated. STR alleles may be homozygous (the alleles have an identical number of repeats) or heterozygous (the alleles have a different number of repeats). STRs are passed down from parents to offspring because the offspring's genome contains half of his father's chromosomes and half of his mother's chromosomes. To use the STR in PCR analysis, the sequences before and after the STR (20–30 bases before and after the STR) must be determined. These sequences are called "flanking regions" (Figure 9.2).

It is critical to understand that flanking regions do not change from individual to individual within a species. Also, these flanking regions are unique to the STR because each STR has a unique locus on a chromosome. Oligonucleotides complementary to the flanking regions are synthesized and used as the primers in the PCR. It is important to understand that primers are specific to a given STR, because the flanking regions around each STR are different.

The resulting PCR products are compared on a gel. If the individual is homozygous, both alleles are the same size and the result is a single PCR product and a single band on the gel. If the individual is heterozygous, the alleles have a different number of repeats and the result will be two PCR products and two bands on the gel (Figure 9.3). Each STR can have many alleles, depending on the genetic diversity of the population, but each individual can only have two alleles because only two alleles can be represented in a pair of chromosomes.

Each STR reveals genetic information on only one locus in the genome, therefore looking at the results of a PCR from one set of STR primers does not reveal a unique identity. To create a DNA profile of an individual using STRs, many STR loci must be amplified by PCR and analyzed.

Advantages of Short Tandem Repeats

DNA fingerprinting using Short Tandem Repeats has several advantages over traditional DNA fingerprinting. First, analysis is possible from very small amounts of starting DNA. Since the DNA to be analyzed will be amplified millions of times, it is theoretically possible to obtain results from a single copy of DNA. This is more important in forensic crime cases where only traces of evidence, such as a hair or a dried drop of blood, are available. The

---

Allele 1: The sequence AGG is repeated seven times or $[AGG]_7$

5' TACGTACGTA	AGGAGGAGGAGGAGGAGGAGG	AGCTGCATC 3'
Flanking region	**Short Tandem Repeats (STR)**	**Flanking region**

Allele 2: The sequence AGG is repeated five times, or $[AGG]_5$

5' TACGTACGTA	AGGAGGAGGAGGAGG	AGCTGCATC 3'
Flanking region	**Short Tandem Repeats (STR)**	**Flanking region**

Figure 9.2. Short Tandem Repeats (STRs). An example of two alleles for the same STR. The STR is the repeating sequence AGG. Notice that the flanking regions on each side of the STR do not change. The flanking regions are used to make primers to amplify the STR.

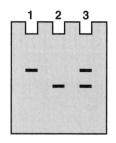

An agarose gel with the three band pattern possibilities for amplified DNA of the STR illustrated in Figure 9.2.

1. An individual homozygous for Allele 1 $[AAG]_7$
2. An individual homozygous for Allele 2 $[AAG]_5$
3. A heterozygous individual with both Allele 1 $[AAG]_7$ and Allele 2 $[AAG]_5$

Figure 9.3. STR Analysis

second is that for PCR, the DNA does not need to be of high quality; it can be old or even degraded. Finally, PCR is relatively easy to perform, it involves no radioactive materials, and results can be obtained within a short time frame, usually within 24 hours.

Laboratory Protocol

PURPOSE

The purpose of this lab is to introduce an application of PCR technology and STR analysis in paternity testing. The class will be divided into groups and will receive four PCR samples to run on an agarose gel and analyze.

Before receiving your samples, make sure you are familiar with the introductory material about whooping cranes, PCR and about short tandem repeats (STRs).

PROCEDURE

You will receive samples of PCR amplified STRs from four whooping cranes. The cranes are a chick (offspring), its mother (called a dam in pedigree analysis), and two potential fathers (called sires in pedigree analysis). There are eight amplified STRs for each bird.

Depending on class size, your group will receive samples from either one or two STRs (remember this is a unique genetic marker). The other groups in your class will receive the other STRs. Your job is to run a gel and analyze the results for these STRs. Your results will be easy to analyze. Because whooping cranes are not genetically diverse, each STR will have one to three alleles. Once all the teams have analyzed their results, the data will be

pooled to create profiles of the birds and determine who the father is.

SETTING UP THE ELECTROPHORESIS CHAMBER

* Place the electrophoresis cell on a sturdy surface.

* Put a sheet of black paper between the cell and the table (you can see better against a dark background).

* Open the ziplock bag and remove the gel. Be sure that the blue stripe on the bag is up—there is a top and a bottom to the gel and the gels have been placed in the bag so that the top is always on the side with the blue stripe. Gels are very slippery and contain ethidium bromide. Be very careful.

* The gel should lie flat in the tray and you should see raised areas corresponding to each well. Note that there are eight wells in one end of the gel. This is where you will load your DNA sample. Be sure you have your TA check your gel before you start.

* Place the tray with the gel in the electrophoresis cell so that the wells are closest to the cathode (the black colored side). Keep the tray horizontal as the gels easily slide out of the tray.

* Check to be sure that the gel is covered by a thin layer of electrophoresis buffer. If not, carefully add buffer so that the gel is covered by a 2–3 mm layer.

- Make sure that the wells are completely filled. If air bubbles persist, carefully tap the well with your gloved finger to remove the bubbles.

LOADING THE WELLS WITH WHOOPING CRANE DNA

- Obtain a pipette tip from the yellow box. Be sure that the tip is firmly placed upon the pipetter.

- Set the micropipetter to 7.00 μl.

- Carefully obtain a whooping crane DNA sample.

- Load the DNA sample into the pre-designated well. This can be tricky—the tip of the micropipetter must be positioned right over the well, not inside it. Additionally, the tip of the micropipetter penetrates the surface of the buffer while you load the well.

- Steady your hand before loading the well.

   - Rest both elbows on the table.

   - The hand that operates the micropipetter is supported by the other one.

- Gently dispense the sample onto the well.

- The sample contains a loading dye to make it visible and heavy. It will go straight down if released gently.

- Eject and discard the micropipetter tip in the appropriate beaker.

WARNING: The tip ejection mechanism can shoot tips at a great distance. Do *not* shoot your lab partner or your TA!

RUNNING THE GEL

- Place the lid on the electrophoresis cell. Be careful with the wires.

- Connect the wires to the power supply.

- Set the appropriate voltage on the power supply—120V.

- Apply power (push the button with the guy running on it). You should see bubbles forming at the black terminal (cathode).

- Run gel for at least one hour.

OBTAINING YOUR RESULTS

- Take the tray out of the cell. Gently tip the tray so the excess buffer will drip back into the cell. Be careful—the gel will slide out of the tray unless you place a finger on the edge.

- Carefully slide the gel onto the UV Transilluminator.

- Close the UV Transilluminator lid.

- Turn the lab's light off.

- Turn the UV Transilluminator on.

- Observe the bands (the door is not transparent to UV light).

- Open the UV Transilluminator lid and place the camera hood over the glass plate. Make sure that the magnetic activator on the camera is to the right side of the plate.

- Press the PRINT button and a picture of your gel will be printed.

- Share your data with the rest of the class in the method explained by your TA.

DISPOSAL OF GELS

- Put the gel back into the ziplock bag.

- Place the ziplock in the "used gels" bin and your TA will dispose of the gels.

ANIMAL ANATOMY AND PHYSIOLOGY

CHAPTER 10

After completing this laboratory, you should be able to:

- Identify the sex and features of the external anatomy of a fetal pig.

- Trace the flow of food through the digestive system.

- Dissect and identify the major components of the digestive system.

- Compare and contrast chemical and physical digestion and know where each occurs in the alimentary canal

- Describe the mechanism and effects of ventilation.

- Identify the parts of the respiratory system.

- Identify the components of the circulatory system.

- Compare and contrast adult and fetal circulation patterns.

- Understand the differences between arteries, capillaries, and veins.

- Identify the major components of the excretory system.

- Compare and contrast the organs and functions of the male and female reproductive systems.

Introduction and Safety

Fetal pigs are unborn fetuses taken from a sow's uterus when she is slaughtered. They are a by-product of pork production, and since the fetus cannot be utilized for human consumption, they are sold to biological supply houses for use in laboratories such as this. Female pigs are NOT purposely impregnated for this purpose—aside from the ethical concerns this would raise, the cost would be prohibitive for a teaching laboratory.

We are using the fetal pig as a model for human anatomy. You may not realize it, but the internal anatomy of a pig is very similar to that of a human. We are both omnivores; i.e., we eat both plant and animal materials. Because of this, our digestive systems are more similar to a pig than ours to a dog (a carnivore) or ours to a cow (an herbivore).

The pigs are preserved in CaroSafe, a formalin derivative, which can irritate your skin, eyes, and nose.

Use appropriate caution—if you wear contact lenses, you may want to remove them before performing this laboratory. Rubber gloves will be provided for your safety—these are most likely latex-free, but if you know you are allergic to latex, please ask your TA first before you put on a pair of gloves.

You will use the same fetal pig for all three laboratory exercises. Most likely, these labs will extend over two or more laboratory periods, so you will have to perform careful dissections and be especially careful in how you pack your fetal pig so it will not become damaged before the next laboratory.

Two bits of advice—(1) The best dissection tools are your gloved fingers. Cut as little as possible to reduce the risk of damaging the organs or cutting important blood vessels and nerves. (2) Do not remove organs unless told to do so.

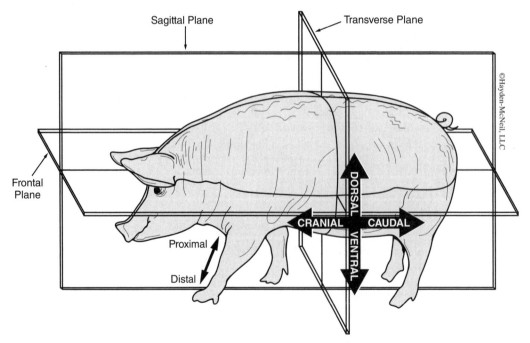

Figure 10.1. Orientation Used in Anatomical Studies

©Hayden-McNeil, LLC

Terminology: Orientation Used in Anatomical Studies

Many of the instructions in this laboratory utilize special terminology, which you should become familiar with. Several examples are given below and in Figure 10.1.

Anterior—situated at or near the head or cranial portion of the organism. In organisms lacking a well-defined head, anterior is defined as the direction of movement.

Posterior—the opposite of anterior. Located near the organism's hind end.

Dorsal—the back side of an organism. In vertebrates, this refers to the side with the spinal column. Opposite of ventral.

Ventral—the belly or lower side of an organism. Opposite of dorsal.

Cephalic (cranial)—referring to the head or in the direction of the head. Opposite of caudal.

Caudal—referring to the tail or in the direction of the tail. Opposite of cephalic.

Proximal—located near the central portion of the body or near the point of attachment. Opposite of distal.

Distal—located away from the central portion of the body or away from the point of attachment. Opposite of proximal.

Medial— a line that divides bilaterally symmetrical organisms into right and left halves. Note that right and left refer to the organism's right and left sides, not yours, the observer's.

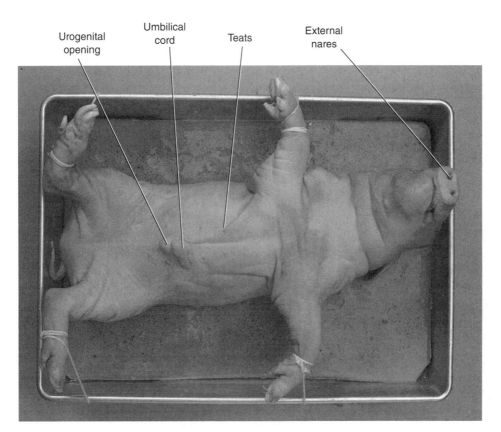

Figure 10.2. Fetal Pig External Anatomy

External Anatomy of the Pig

Your instructor will assign your group a fetal pig. If the pig is sealed in a vacuum sealed plastic bag, you must first cut open a corner of the bag and drain out the excess fluid. There will be disposal containers in the front sink—carefully bring the bag to the container and pour the excess fluid into the container. Return to your station and fully open the bag. If the pig is wrapped with paper towels, remove these and dispose of them in a different container provided by your teaching assistant.

Lay the pig in the dissection tray on its dorsal side so that the belly is exposed. Take some string and tie a double-knot around one arm. Wrap the string under the dissection tray, pulling tight, and then tie down the other arm. Repeat the above procedure with the legs of your pig. Your pig should now be securely tied to the dissection tray and ready for examination (Figure 10.2).

Before you get all excited and cut the pig open, please take some time and observe the external anatomy of the fetal pig.

DETERMINATION OF SEX

Is your pig male or female? How can you tell? Aside from reading the label on the bag, the sex of a fetal pig is easy to determine. Along the ventral surface, you should notice a row of nipples—this does not mean your pig is female! (Guys, you've got nipples too.) Look at the posterior end of the pig (Figure 10.3). Male pigs have a pronounced **scrotal sac** (the pig on the left in Figure 10.3 is male). Also, if you look under the tail, there is just one opening, the anus. The **urethral opening** is posterior to the umbilical cord. There should be a small enlargement here, possibly with a few tufts of hair. This is from where the male pig would urinate and from where the penis would extend. Females have a **urogenital sinus** ventral to the anus (the pig on the right in Figure 10.3 is female). The urogenital sinus is the opening containing the urethral and vaginal openings. Ventral to the urogenital sinus is the **genital papillae**.

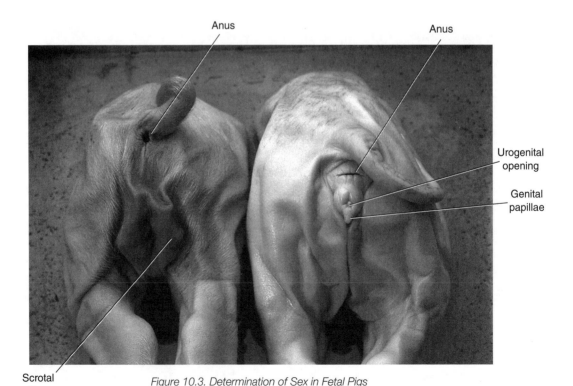

Anus Anus

Urogenital opening

Genital papillae

Scrotal Sac

Figure 10.3. Determination of Sex in Fetal Pigs

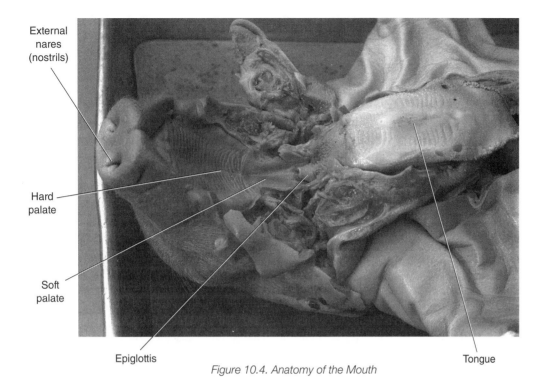

External
nares
(nostrils)

Hard
palate

Soft
palate

Epiglottis

Tongue

Figure 10.4. Anatomy of the Mouth

EXTERNAL ANATOMY

Locate the nostrils, or **external nares**, on the snout of the pig. The tongue should be partially extended; note the **lingual papillae**, which aid the pig in tasting food. You should notice the **umbilical cord** extending from the ventral surface of the pig. If your pig is male, you should note the urogenital opening ventral to the umbilical cord attachment. Two rows of six nipples should be seen. Finally, lift the tail and you should see the **anus**. If your pig is female, you should notice the urogenital sinus ventral to the anus.

ANATOMY OF THE MOUTH

Carefully open the mouth. Use scissors to cut open both sides at the corner of the mouth. It may be difficult to cut through the mandible, so be careful. Extend the cut to a point just past the eye. Pry open the lower jaw until a flap of tissue pops from the throat. Your pig should look like Figure 10.4. Observe the **hard palate**, the portion of the "roof of the mouth" that is based by the sphenoid bone. Progress caudal into the throat and you will notice the **soft palate**. If you curl your tongue up in your mouth, you may be able to distinguish the transition between hard and soft palate in your own mouth.

The tissue that popped from the throat is the **epiglottis**. Mammals eat and breathe through the mouth. The common passageway of the respiratory and digestive tracts is the **pharynx**. Food will continue down the digestive tract through the **esophagus**. Air will continue down to the lungs via the **trachea**. The epiglottis is a muscular flap that regulates which passageway food and air will travel. The default position is the epiglottis blocking the esophagus and leaving the trachea open. You breathe more often than you eat, so this is logical. However, when you swallow food or water, the epiglottis moves and covers the trachea, leaving the esophagus open. If you put your hand on your throat when you swallow, you can feel the epiglottis move.

ANATOMY OF THE ALIMENTARY CANAL AND ASSOCIATED ORGANS

Now you must open up the body of the pig. To begin, use the scissors and make a small cut in the throat of the pig. Use your fingers to open the hole a bit. Insert the scissors in the hole and cut the ventral surface toward the posterior end. Be careful not to go too deep and cut the trachea. Continue posterior cutting until you come parallel to the arms. Here you are going to have to cut through the bones of the rib cage. The bones are soft, so it should not be too difficult. Don't cut too deeply or you will damage the heart.

Continue cutting in a posterior direction until you come close to the **umbilical cord**. Here you will cut around the umbilical cord on both sides. Carefully continue cutting on the left side and then the right side, about halfway around the umbilical cord. If you pull up on the cord, you should see a blood vessel attached on the inside end of the umbilical cord and extending to the liver. This is the **umbilical vein**. It is involved in fetal circulation. Note the identity of this blood vessel and cut it in the middle, leaving free ends on the umbilical and liver sides. Gently pull back on the umbilical cord. You should see a pouch-like organ with blood vessels on either side attaching to the posterior end of the internal umbilical cord. This organ is the **urinary bladder**. Stick a blunt probe in the space between the body

cavity wall and the urinary bladder and cut away the body wall on either side of the umbilical cord. You should end up with the urinary bladder attaching to a round piece of body wall with the umbilical cord attached on the outside. Do not cut any more in the posterior direction. You will come back to these organs in future laboratories.

The body cavity is divided into an upper **thoracic** cavity and a lower **abdominal** cavity. The thoracic cavity contains the heart and the lungs. The abdominal cavity contains the digestive, excretory, and many of the reproductive organs. The two are separated by a large muscle, the **diaphragm**. Find the diaphragm and cut the body wall dorsally just posterior to the diaphragm. The body cavity may be filled with fluid—it is ok to allow this fluid to drain. If necessary, make another pair of cuts just anterior to the legs. This will allow you to have a much better view of the organs (**viscera**) of the abdominal cavity (Figure 10.5).

110

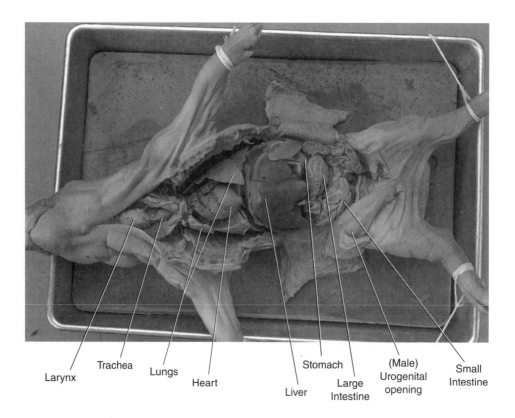

Larynx   Trachea   Lungs   Heart   Liver   Stomach   Large Intestine   (Male) Urogenital opening   Small Intestine

Figure 10.5. Anatomy of the Thoracic and Abdominal Cavities

As you cut into the abdominal wall, you should see the thin **peritoneal membrane**. The dark brown, multi-lobed **liver** will be just posterior to the diaphragm, located on the pig's right side. Gently lift the liver and you should see the dark green-colored **gall bladder** on the underside of the liver. The liver serves a variety of functions, including detoxifying the blood, production of some digestive enzymes, and the formation of **bile**. Bile, a chemical which emulsifies fats to aid in digestion, is produced in the liver but stored in the gall bladder.

Under the liver on the left side of the pig is the **stomach**. Locate the point where the esophagus enters the **cardiac region** of the stomach. Here food is digested through physical and chemical means. Hydrochloric acid is secreted by the stomach to kill bacteria and acidify the stomach. Pepsinogen is secreted by the stomach and when it enters the acidic environment, it becomes pepsin, an enzyme that digests proteins. The muscular stomach churns the food, mixing it with enzymes and physically breaking it into smaller portions. It leaves the stomach as liquid **chyme**. The **pyloric sphincter** is a muscular ring which can open and close, allowing small amounts of chyme to enter the next organ of the alimentary canal, the **small intestine**.

The small intestine is composed of three portions, in order, the **duodenum**, the **jejunum**, and the **ileum** (Figure 10.6). These three areas are difficult to distinguish from each other, however. The duodenum is the first portion and it is here that the acidic chyme is neutralized by sodium bicarbonate secretions. Find where the stomach interfaces with the small intestine; this is the duodenum. The jejunum is where the majority of digestion and absorption takes place in the small intestine. The ileum is the final portion. Follow the small intestine from beginning to end and where the small intestine meets the large intestine is the final portion of the ileum. The lining of the small intestine is festooned with **villi**, small, finger-like projections that dramatically increase the surface area of the small intestine (Figure 10.7). Remember that absorption is a surface area phenomena—the more surface area present, the more efficient the organ will be at absorption.

The small intestine does not join the **large intestine**, or **colon**, end to end. Instead, there is a T-intersection-like joining. The blind end of the colon is the **cecum**. At the terminal end of the cecum is the **appendix**. Digestion is mostly complete when food leaves the small intestine. The function of the large intestine is reclaiming water and electrolytes from the digestive wastes. This process, **compaction**, dehydrates the digested food, forming **feces**. The **rectum** is at the caudal end of the large intestine. It is a large, muscular sac, which stores feces. Two sphincters, one voluntary and one involuntary, control the release of feces from the body through the anus in a process known as **elimination**.

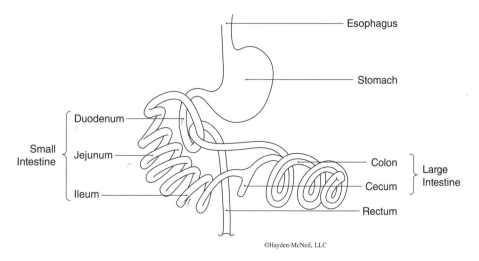

©Hayden-McNeil, LLC

Figure 10.6. The Large and Small Intestines

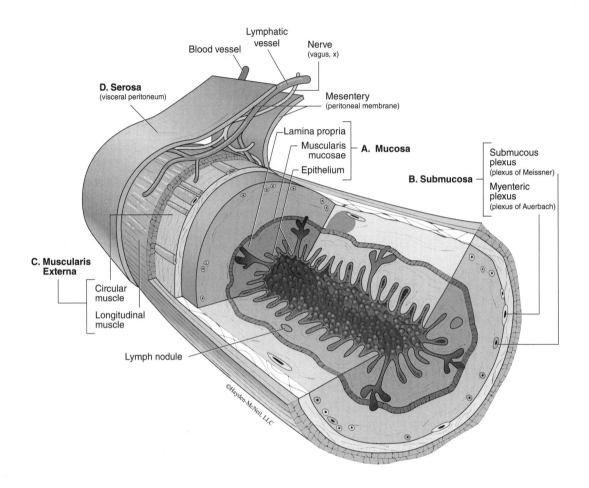

Figure 10.7. Internal Anatomy of the Small Intestine

ANATOMY OF THE THROAT

Carefully open up the throat. You should see something similar to Figure 10.8. The large, centrally located cartilaginous structure is the **larynx**. This is the "voice box," which enables pigs to oink and humans to speak. Inside the larynx are two **vocal chords** that vibrate as air passes through them, allowing the formation of sound. Separate the muscles just anterior to the larynx. You should see a dark brown-colored structure, the **thyroid gland**. The thyroid gland secretes several classes of hormones, including those involved in growth. Remove the thyroid and look at the tube beneath. This is the **trachea**. The trachea is the passageway through which air flows from the pharynx toward the lungs. The trachea is supported by cartilaginous rings—air is not viscous enough to keep the trachea open. Run your finger over the trachea—you should feel the cartilaginous rings. The trachea continues posterior where it splits, forming two **bronchial tube**s.

Under the trachea you should find the **esophagus**. The esophagus is relatively flat—when food or liquid passes through, the muscles lining the esophagus contract and relax, forcing the food down to the stomach in a process known as **peristalsis**. If you are having difficulty finding the esophagus, pass a blunt probe down the throat to help inflate the esophagus. Distal to the trachea and esophagus, you should see large organs that extend posterior into the thoracic cavity. These are the **thymus glands**, which are involved in T-cell formation.

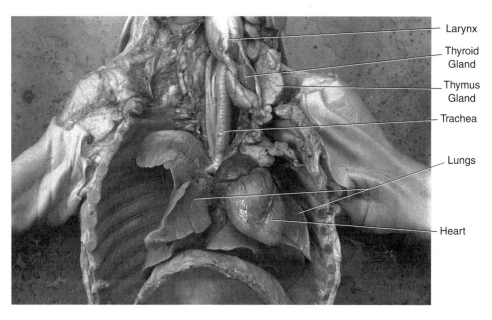

Larynx

Thyroid
Gland

Thymus
Gland

Trachea

Lungs

Heart

Figure 10.8. Anatomy of the Throat and Thoracic Cavity

ANATOMY OF THE RESPIRATORY SYSTEM

The bronchial tubes will merge with two large organs, the **lungs**. Since you are observing a fetal pig, the lungs are not inflated. Inside the lungs, the bronchial tubes continue to split again and again until they terminate in highly vascularized, blind pouches known as **alveoli** (Figure 10.9). The capillaries surrounding the alveoli facilitate gas exchange.

MECHANISM OF VENTILATION

The **diaphragm** is a sheet of muscle that separates the thoracic cavity from the abdominal cavity. Air enters the lungs through the coordinated efforts of the diaphragm and **intercostal** (between the ribs) muscles. During inhalation, the diaphragm and intercostal muscles contract, increasing the volume of the thoracic cavity. The lungs are attached to the body walls by mesenteries, and this increase in volume creates a vacuum. Nature abhors a vacuum, so air rushes into the lungs. During exhalation, the diaphragm and intercostal muscles relax. The relaxing muscles reduce the size of the thoracic cavity, forcing air out (Figure 10.10). During inhalation, the pressure of the lungs is less than the outside atmosphere, so air passively flows in. During exhalation, pressure inside the lungs is greater than the outside atmosphere, so air is forced out.

The Circulatory System

The circulatory system in mammals consists of a fluid, **blood**, which flows through a series of **blood vessels**, powered by a pump called the **heart**. The mammalian circulatory system is a **closed circulatory system** because the blood flow never leaves the blood vessels. Some invertebrates have an **open circulatory system** consisting of a pumping system that bathes the organs in a blood-like fluid called **hemolymph**.

The circulatory system has a diverse array of functions. First, it is closely associated with the respiratory system in its function of carrying oxygen and removing carbon dioxide from bodily tissues. Second, the circulatory system is closely associated with the digestive system. Food digested must be absorbed and the nutrients transported throughout the body. This is accomplished by the circulatory system. The circulatory system also serves as a thoroughfare for the cells of the immune system to travel throughout the body and destroy pathogens. Likewise, the endocrine system utilizes the circulatory system as a means of transport of hormones. Finally, the circulatory system is involved in thermoregulation and the transport of heat throughout the body.

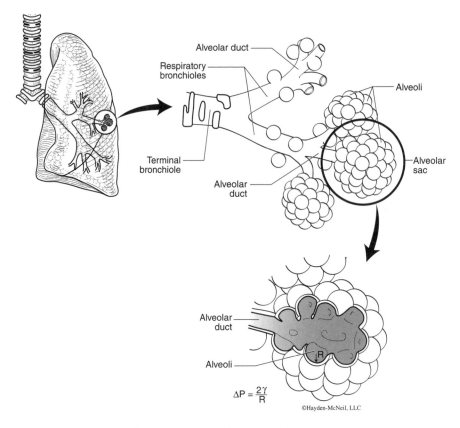

Figure 10.9. Internal Anatomy of the Lungs

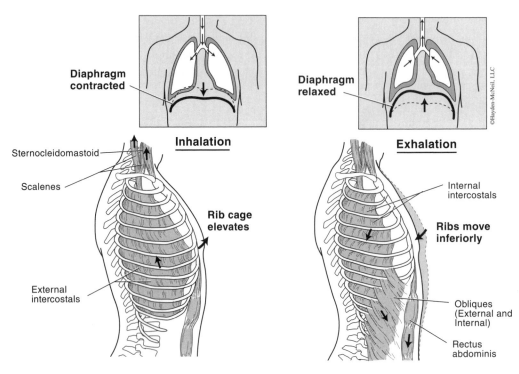

Figure 10.10. Inhalation and Exhalation

BLOOD VESSELS

There are five types of blood vessels that constitute the vascular portion of the circulatory system: arteries, arterioles, capillaries, venules, and veins. **Arteries** and **arterioles** are thick-walled blood vessels that are defined as vessels that carry blood *away* from the heart. Arteries are the larger of the two—when they branch, they form smaller diameter arterioles. Arteries and arterioles have muscular, elastic walls that help maintain blood pressure. Arterioles will become more finely branched, eventually forming thin-walled **capillaries**. Capillary walls are only one cell layer thick, which enables oxygen and carbon dioxide to diffuse down their concentration gradients, thus oxygenating cells and removing toxic wastes. Additionally, leucocytes can squeeze through the "leaky" capillary walls and enter tissues. Capillaries join together to form **venules**, which further join to form **veins**. Venules and veins are defined as blood vessels that carry blood back *toward* the heart. Blood pressure in veins is very low, so they have valves inside which prevent back flow. Contraction of skeletal muscles also aids blood flow in veins as it returns to the heart.

In the systemic circuit, blood in arteries is oxygenated and blood in veins is deoxygenated. However, in the pulmonary circuit, blood in arteries is deoxygenated while the blood in veins is oxygenated.

ANATOMY OF THE HEART

The heart is the large, muscular organ located between the lungs (Figure 10.11). It is surrounded by a thick, fluid-filled membrane, the **pericardial sac** (also known as the **pericardium**). You probably tore the pericardium when you were opening up the chest. You may also notice that the pericardium is attached to the sternum. This is to firmly attach the heart so its active beating does not damage fragile blood vessels or deflate the lungs.

The function of the heart is to pump blood throughout the body. The heart is actually two pumps in one—the right side of the heart pumps blood from the heart to the lungs and back (the **pulmonary circuit**) while the left side of the heart pumps blood from the heart to the body and back (the **systemic**

circuit). The mammalian heart has four chambers. The upper two, the **left and right atria** (singular = atrium), are thin-walled chambers that collect blood as it returns to the heart and pump it to the lower two chambers, the **left and right ventricles**. Ventricles pump blood to the lungs or to the body.

FLOW OF BLOOD THROUGH THE HEART— THE PULMONARY CIRCUIT

Deoxygenated blood enters the right atrium from two blood vessels, the **cranial** and **caudal vena cava**. (Note, in humans, these two blood vessels are called the **superior** and **inferior vena cava**. This is simply due to the fact that humans walk erect while most mammals are quadrupedal.) The right atrium contracts, forcing the blood through the **right atrioventricular (tricuspid) valve** and into the **right ventricle**. The right ventricle contracts, forcing blood through the **pulmonary semilunar valve** and into the **pulmonary trunk**. The pulmonary trunk splits, forming the **left** and **right pulmonary arteries**. These carry deoxygenated blood to the lungs. Oxygenated blood returns to the left side of the heart via the **pulmonary veins**.

FLOW OF BLOOD THROUGH THE HEART— THE SYSTEMIC CIRCUIT

Oxygenated blood returns to the heart via the pulmonary veins (note—the pulmonary veins are very small and difficult to see in a fetal pig). Blood enters the **left atrium**. The left atrium contracts, forcing blood through the **left atrioventricular (bicuspid) valve** into the **left ventricle**. The left ventricle contracts, forcing blood through the **aortic semilunar valve** and into the **aorta**. The aorta is the largest blood vessel in the body. From the aorta, blood can travel throughout the body.

DIFFERENCES BETWEEN PIG AND HUMAN AORTAL BRANCHING

The first branches of the aorta feed the head, upper body, and arms. However, there are differences between the aortal branches of a pig and a human. In a pig, there are two aortal branches, the **brachiocephalic trunk** and the **left subclavian artery** (Figure 10.12). The left subclavian artery carries blood to the left arm (subclavian means "under the clavicle," the

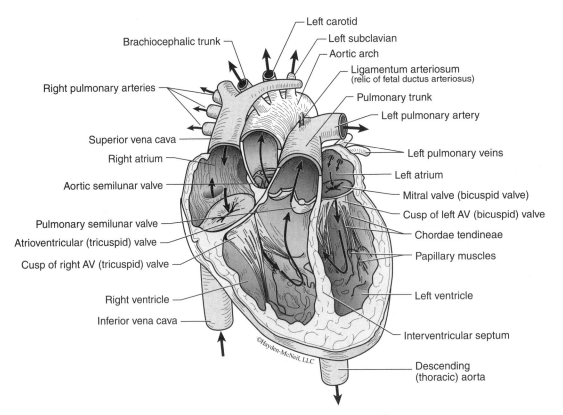

Brachiocephalic trunk

Left carotid

Left subclavian

Aortic arch

Ligamentum arteriosum
(relic of fetal ductus arteriosus)

Right pulmonary arteries

Pulmonary trunk

Left pulmonary artery

Superior vena cava

Left pulmonary veins

Right atrium

Left atrium

Aortic semilunar valve

Mitral valve (bicuspid valve)

Cusp of left AV (bicuspid) valve

Pulmonary semilunar valve

Chordae tendineae

Atrioventricular (tricuspid) valve

Papillary muscles

Cusp of right AV (tricuspid) valve

Right ventricle

Left ventricle

Inferior vena cava

Interventricular septum

©Hayden-McNeil, LLC

Descending
(thoracic) aorta

Figure 10.11. Flow of Blood through a Human Heart

clavicle commonly known as the collar bone). The brachiocephalic trunk branches three times, forming the **right subclavian** (feeding the right arm), the **right carotid** (feeding the right side of the head) and the **left carotid** (feeding the left side of the head).

In humans, the aorta has three branches, the **brachiocephalic trunk**, the **left carotid**, and the **left subclavian**. The brachiocephalic trunk branches to form the **right subclavian** and **right carotid** arteries. The only difference between the pig and humans is the branching of the left carotid, from the brachiocephalic trunk in pigs and directly from the aorta in humans. Models of the human heart and Figures 10.11 and 10.12 should help you differentiate between what you see in the pig and the flow of blood in humans.

FLOW OF BLOOD THROUGH THE BODY—MAJOR ARTERIES

Blood leaves the left side of the heart through the **aorta**. Trace the aorta as it arches behind the heart, traveling posteriorly. You will have to lift up the lungs to see the aorta. There are major branches of the aorta, including the **hepatic artery** (to the liver), the **renal arteries** (to the kidneys). At the legs, the aorta splits in two, forming the **left** and **right iliac arteries**, which supply blood to the legs.

FETAL CIRCULATION

The oxygenation and circulation of a fetus differs from that of an adult. In an adult, blood is oxygenated in the lungs. However, in a fetus, blood is oxygenated in the **placenta**. Blood reaches the placenta through two **umbilical arteries**. If you locate the urinary bladder, you will see two umbilical arteries flanking the bladder (Figure 10.16). The umbilical

Left Carotid Artery
Left Subclavian Artery
Ductus Arteriosis
Descending Branch of Aorta
Renal Artery

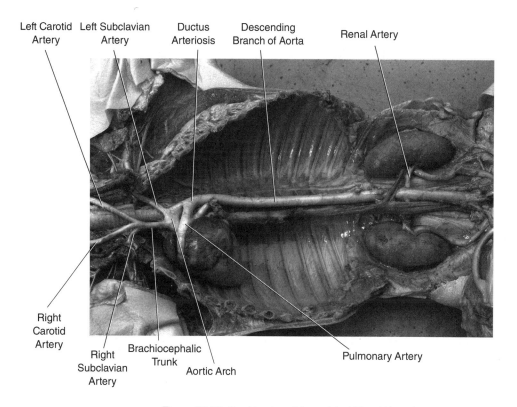

Right Carotid Artery
Right Subclavian Artery
Brachiocephalic Trunk
Aortic Arch
Pulmonary Artery

Figure 10.12. The Heart and Associated Blood Vessels

arteries carry deoxygenated blood to the placenta where it becomes oxygenated. Oxygenated blood returns to the body through the **umbilical vein.** You should remember cutting the umbilical vein when you opened up the abdominal cavity.

The umbilical vein rejoins the fetus' circulation system at the **ductus venosus.** Oxygenated blood then enters the **hepatic portal vein** and eventuallymakes its way to the **caudal vena cava,** where it enters the heart.

In an adult, all of the blood entering the right side of the heart would be pumped to the lungs to become oxygenated. However, since blood is oxygenated in the placenta, there is no need for all of the blood to enter the lungs. There are two shunts that allow most of the blood to bypass the lungs and enter into the systemic circuit, transporting the oxygenated

blood throughout the body. When the right atrium contracts, some of the blood will pass through the right atrioventricular valve and enter the right ventricle. However, most of the blood will pass through a pore in the wall separating the left and right atria, the **foramen ovale.** Blood passing through the foramen ovale is now in the left, or systemic, side of the heart and will flow to the rest of the body. Blood that passed to the right ventricle will be forced through the pulmonary semilunar valve and enter the pulmonary trunk. In adults, this blood would be destined for the lungs. However, it is here that the second shunt, the **ductus arteriosus,** is found. The ductus arteriosus is a connection between the pulmonary trunk and the aorta. Most of the blood in the pulmonary trunk will pass through the ductus arteriosus and enter the aorta (which is part of the systemic circuit). A minimal amount of blood will continue on through the pulmonary circuit and enter the lungs.

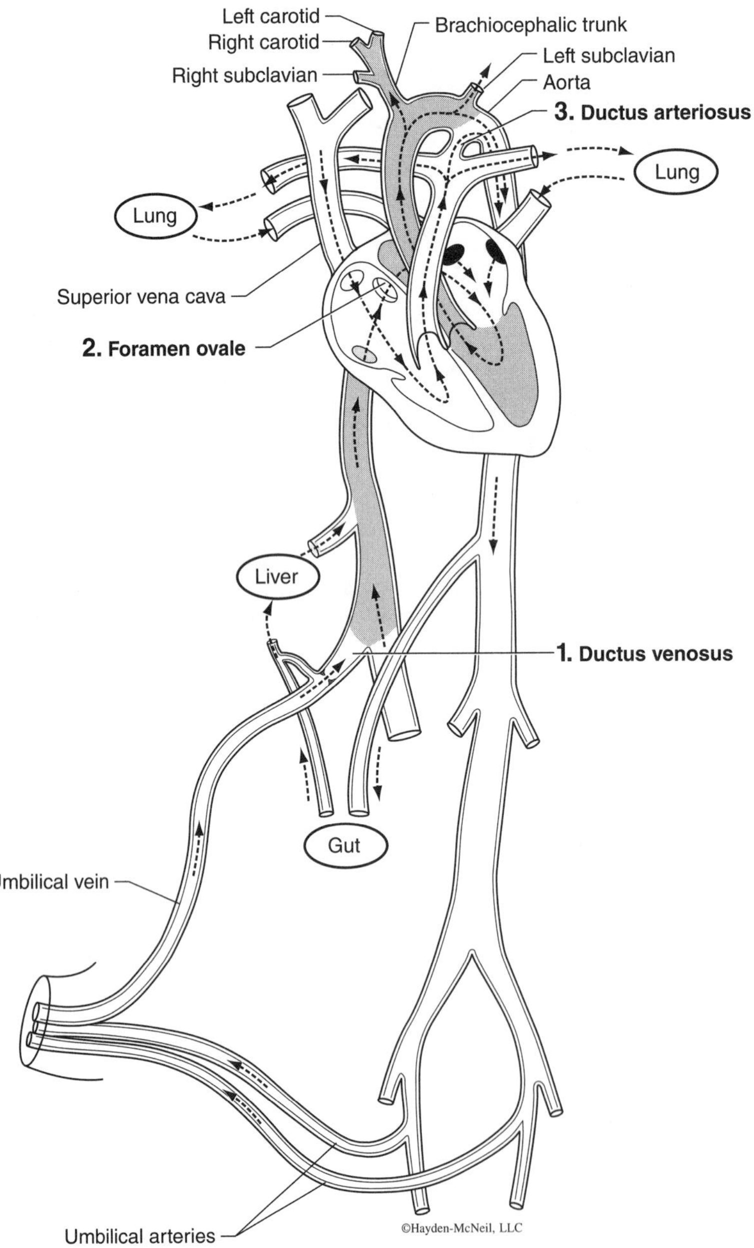

Fetal Circulation

Umbilical vein blood mixed only with blood from inferior vena cava and liver (a very minor flow of blood from the non-functional lungs is added from the left atrium)

Figure 10.13. Circulation of the Fetal Pig

Anatomy of the Excretory System

The **kidneys** are large, bean-shaped organs located on the dorsal wall of the abdominal cavity, under the large and small intestines (Figure 10.14). You will have to remove the **peritoneum** in order to better see them. Observe the **renal arteries** and **renal veins**, taking blood to and from the kidneys. Find the **ureter**, a large, yellowish tubule on the medial face of each kidney. Trace the ureter as it flows into the **urinary bladder**. The urinary bladder should be flanked on the sagittal faces by two **umbilical arteries**. The urinary bladder is a large storage organ for **urine**, the waste products of blood filtration (see below). Urine leaves the body through the **urethra**. Trace the urethra from the urinary bladder to the **penis** or **vagina**, depending upon the sex of your pig. To better observe the urethra, you will have to carefully cut through the pelvic girdle. Pressing down on the legs may help you in this endeavor.

HISTOLOGY OF THE KIDNEY

Carefully remove a kidney and cut it in half along the frontal plane (i.e., the long way). Observe the **renal capsule, cortex, medulla, renal artery, renal vein**, and **ureter**.

BLOOD FLOW AND FILTRATION IN A NEPHRON

The primary function of the kidney is filtering the blood. Blood enters the kidney through the **renal artery**. From there, the renal artery branches many times to form **glomerular capillaries**, where blood plasma is squeezed out, filtered in a nephron, and then the filtrate reabsorbed (Figure 10.15). The **afferent arteriole** brings blood into the **glomerulus**. The walls of the glomerular capillaries are very leaky and the blood pressure remains high, so the liquid plasma is squeezed out into the **Bowman's Capsule**. The glomerular capillaries join together and form the **efferent arterioles**.

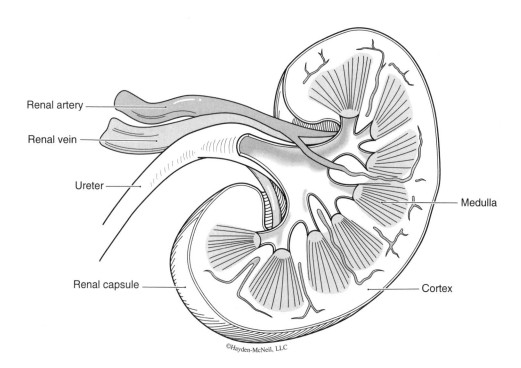

©Hayden-McNeil, LLC

Figure 10.14. Anatomy of the Mammalian Kidney

Plasma in the glomerulus flows down the **proximal convoluted tubule**. From there it enters the **Loop of Henle**. The Loop of Henle extends down from the cortex into the medulla of the kidney where the blood plasma is reabsorbed by the **peritubular capillaries (vasa recta)**. The reconstituted blood then leaves the kidney through the **renal vein**. The waste materials (urine) left behind leave the Loop of Henle, enter the **distal convoluted tubule** (more reabsorption takes place here). Finally, the urine in the distal convoluted tubule joins the **collecting duct**, which will eventually join the **ureter**.

The Reproductive Systems

If your pig is male, proceed to the male reproductive system section below. If your pig is female, skip this section and proceed to the female reproductive system below. Be sure that when you are done, you observe the reproductive system of the other gender. Simply trade pigs with another group or observe a demonstration pig on the main bench.

THE MALE REPRODUCTIVE SYSTEM

Use the illustration and photograph in Figures 10.16a and 10.16b to aid you in the dissection of the male reproductive system. To find the testes in a male pig, you must first continue your cut surrounding the umbilical cord posteriorly toward the scrotal sac, stopping when you reach the sac. Insert a blunt probe into the scrotal sac and you should find the testes and associated organs wrapped in a membrane called the **cremasteric pouch**. Gently pry open the cremasteric pouch and free the structures inside. You should see a bean-shaped organ—this is the **testis**. Surrounding the testis is the **epididymis**, a tightly coiled mass of tissue. Sperm originate in the testis and then travel to the epididymis where they mature. The epididymis flows into the **vas deferens**. Trace the vas deferens as it leaves the scrotal area and enters the abdominal cavity through the **inguinal canal**. When the testes first develop, they are formed in the abdominal cavity. During maturation, they are pulled into the scrotal sac through the inguinal canal, by a ligament known as the **gubernaculum**.

Continue to trace the vas deferens as it passes by the ureters and enters the urethra. You should be able to see the paired **seminal vesicles** and the single **prostate gland**. Continuing down the urethra, you should see the **Cowper's gland (bulbourethral gland)**. These three glandular systems secrete additional nutrients and fluids into the semen, which carries the sperm during ejaculation. The **penis** of a fetal pig lies deep within the muscular layers. It is quite possible that you have cut the penis when you made your initial cuts around the umbilical cord.

THE FEMALE REPRODUCTIVE SYSTEM

Use the illustration in Figure 10.17 to aid you in the dissection of the female reproductive system. The **ovaries** are bean-shaped organs on the dorsal wall near the kidneys. The ovaries are suspended by two sheets of connective tissue, the **broad ligaments**. On the dorsal side of each ovary is a **fallopian tube (uterine horns)**. The fallopian tubes end in a flower-like structure, the **infundibulum**. Eggs bursting from the ovaries must float across the small space between the ovary and the fallopian tubule. The infundibulum helps to funnel the egg into the fallopian tubule where fertilization takes place. If the egg is fertilized, it will become implanted in the blood-engorged walls of the muscular **uterus** known as the **endometrium**. Fetal development occurs in the uterus. The opening of the uterus to the outside is a muscular tube, the **vagina**. The **cervix**, a tight muscular ring, separates the uterus from the vagina. The vagina serves as the birth canal as well as an entry point for the penis in sexual reproduction. The vagina and the urethra open into a common area known as the **urogenital sinus**.

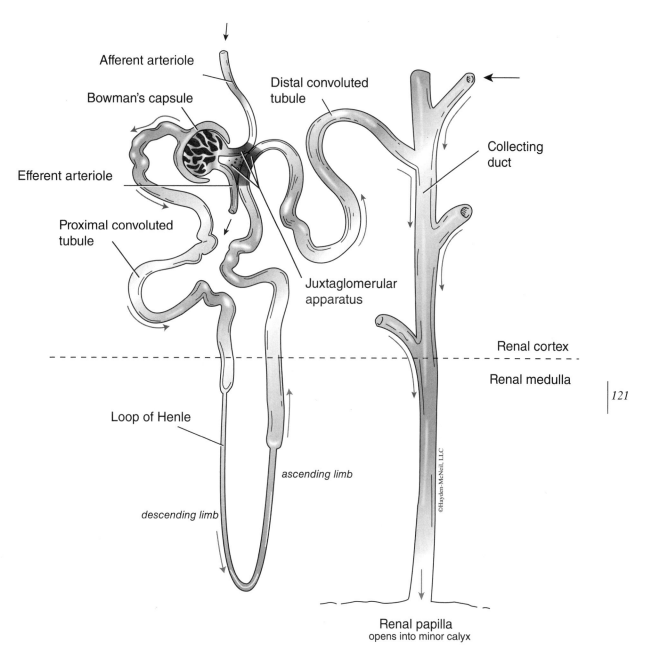

Afferent arteriole

Bowman's capsule

Distal convoluted tubule

Efferent arteriole

Collecting duct

Proximal convoluted tubule

Juxtaglomerular apparatus

Renal cortex

Renal medulla

Loop of Henle

ascending limb

descending limb

©Hayden-McNeil, LLC

Renal papilla
opens into minor calyx

Figure 10.15. Anatomy of a Nephron

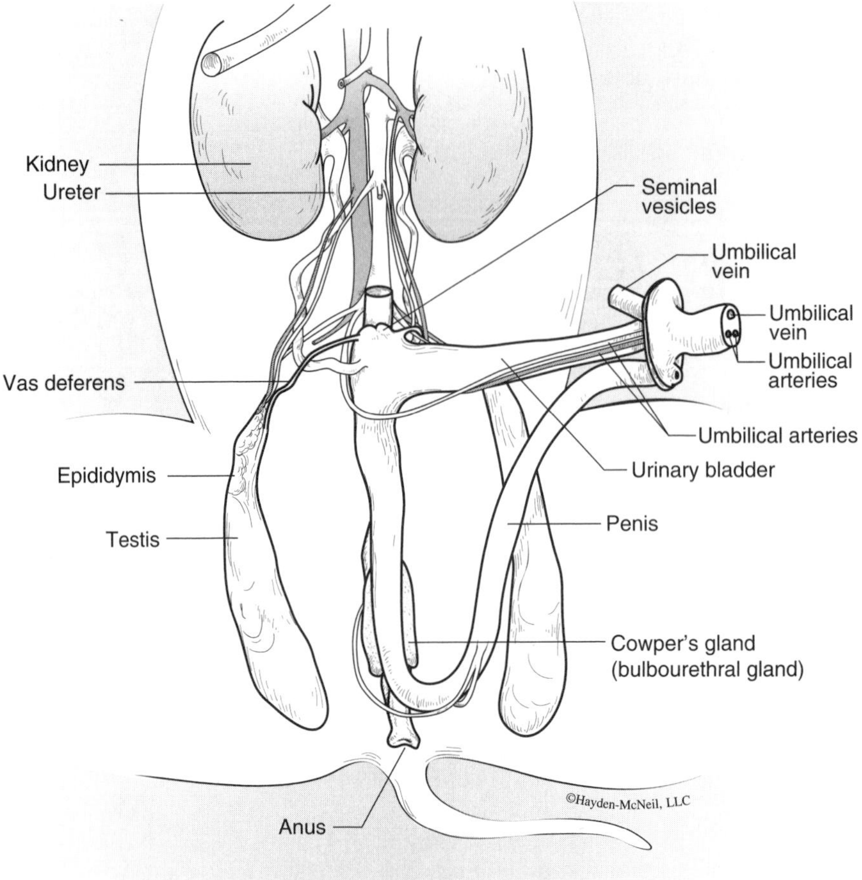

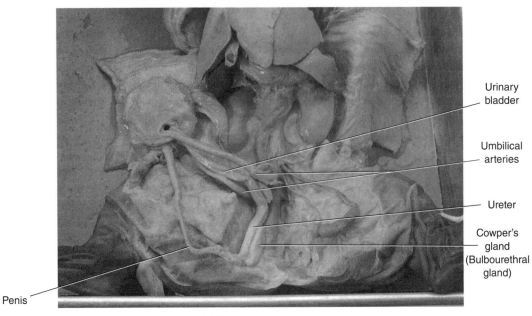

Kidney
Ureter
Seminal vesicles
Umbilical vein
Umbilical vein
Umbilical arteries
Vas deferens
Umbilical arteries
Urinary bladder
Epididymis
Penis
Testis
Cowper's gland (bulbourethral gland)
©Hayden-McNeil, LLC
Anus

Figure 10.16a. Male Pig Internal Anatomy

Urinary bladder

Umbilical arteries

Ureter

Cowper's gland (Bulbourethral gland)

Penis

Figure 10.16b. Male Pig Internal Anatomy

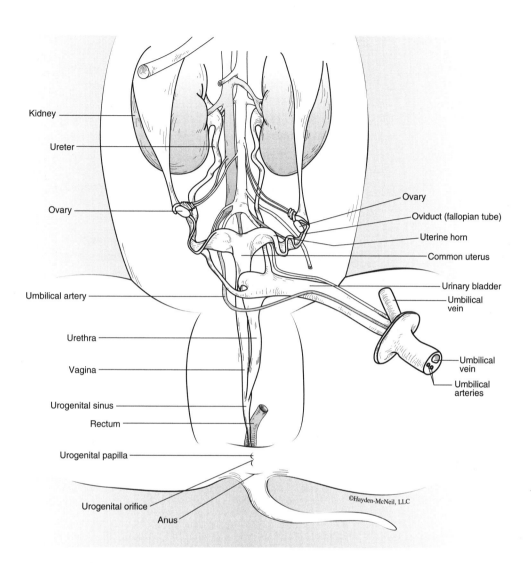

Kidney

Ureter

Ovary

Umbilical artery

Urethra

Vagina

Urogenital sinus

Rectum

Urogenital papilla

Urogenital orifice

Anus

Ovary

Oviduct (fallopian tube)

Uterine horn

Common uterus

Urinary bladder

Umbilical
vein

Umbilical
vein

Umbilical
arteries

©Hayden-McNeil, LLC

123

Figure 10.17. Female Pig Internal Anatomy

Pig Dissection Checklist

External Anatomy
External Nares ___
Umbilical Cord ___
Anus ___
Scrotum (♂) ___
Vaginal Opening (♀) ___

Anatomy of the Mouth
Hard Palate ___
Soft Palate ___
Tongue ___
Epiglottis ___

Digestive System
Esophagus ___
Stomach ___
Small Intestine ___
    Duodenum ___
    Jejunum ___
    Ileum ___
Large Intestine ___
Rectum ___

Associated Organs
Thyroid Gland ___
Liver ___
Gall Bladder ___
Pancreas ___
Spleen ___

Respiratory Organs
Trachea ___
Larynx ___
Lungs ___
Diaphragm ___

Circulatory System
Pericardial Sac ___
Cranial Vena Cava ___
Caudal Vena Cava ___
Right Atrium ___
Left Atrium ___
Right Ventricle ___
Left Ventricle ___
Pulmonary Arteries ___
Aorta ___
Bracheocephalic A. ___
Right Carotid A. ___
Right Subclavian A. ___
Left Carotid A. ___
Left Subclavian A. ___
Ductus Arteriosis ___
Umbilical Artery ___
Umbilical Vein ___

Excretory System
Kidneys ___
Ureters ___
Urinary Bladder ___
Urethra ___
Inguinal Canal ___

Male Reproductive
Testis ___
Epididymis ___
Gubernaculum ___
Vas Deferens ___
Penis ___

Female Reproductive
Ovaries ___
Infundibulum ___
Fallopian Tubes ___
Uterus ___
Cervix ___
Vagina ___

FORM AND FUNCTION IN PHOTOSYNTHESIS

C H A P T E R   1 1

When this lab is completed, students should be able to do the following:

- Observe and describe the morphology and anatomy of angiosperm leaves.

- Be able to compare and contrast monocot and dicot leaves.

- Measure and discuss the absorption properties of chlorophyll.

- Determine the physiological compensation point of *Elodea* leaves.

Background

Photosynthesis, the conversion of light energy to chemical energy, supplies the energy fueling almost every ecosystem on Earth. Plants are **producers**, using energy obtained through photosynthesis for growth, maintenance, and reproduction. Herbivores, animals that eat plants, consume the plants, thus fueling their energy needs. Higher trophic levels are supplied with energy by consuming these lower trophic levels. However, the ultimate source of energy for these higher trophic levels is still photosynthesis.

The primary organelle of photosynthesis is the chloroplast (Figure 11.1). The chloroplast contains three membranes—the **outer** and **inner envelopes** and the **thylakoid membrane**. The outer and inner envelopes surround the chloroplast while the thylakoid membrane is a highly convoluted membrane system arranged in flattened discs known as **grana**. The space enclosed by the thylakoid membrane is known as the thylakoid space. The fluid found inside of the chloroplast is known as the **stroma**.

In photosynthesis, energy in the form of light (photons), is absorbed by special molecules called pigments. Green plants, many algae, and some bacteria contain **chlorophyll**, a pigment that can absorb many wavelengths of visible light and transfer that energy to electrons. These electrons can perform cellular work by passing down an **electron transport chain** (Figure 11.2). The electron transport chain is a series of molecules found bound to the thylakoid membranes that can pump H^+ into the thylakoid space, which serves as a potential energy source for **chemiosmosis**, the creation of ATP. This process is very similar to chemiosmosis in the mitochondria, described in Chapter 7. Ultimately, the final electron acceptor is a molecule of $NADP^+$, which becomes reduced to form a molecule of NADPH. The electron that reduced $NADP^+$ is replaced by splitting a water molecule, forming H^+, electrons, and O_2 gas. This is the source of the oxygen produced by photosynthesis. These reactions are known as the **light-dependent reactions** of photosynthesis.

ATP and NADPH are energy molecules that can be used by plants to construct sugars. Carbon dioxide is taken from the atmosphere and, in a reaction cycle known as the **Calvin Cycle**, energy from NADPH and ATP are used to fuel the construction of the sugar glucose. The Calvin Cycle and associated reactions are known as the **light-independent reactions** of photosynthesis. These are summarized in Figure 11.3.

An important byproduct of photosynthesis is oxygen. Oxygen and carbon dioxide are linked in a biogeochemical cycle—during photosynthesis, plants take in carbon dioxide and produce oxygen. During aerobic respiration, oxygen is taken in and carbon dioxide is produced. This balance helps to ensure that the levels of oxygen and carbon dioxide in the environment remain constant. However, the recent burning of fossil fuels has dramatically increased the amount of carbon dioxide in the atmosphere, which has been a primary cause for global warming. The impact of this input of carbon dioxide in the atmosphere has yet to be fully comprehended, but has already led to changes in climate and rainfall patterns.

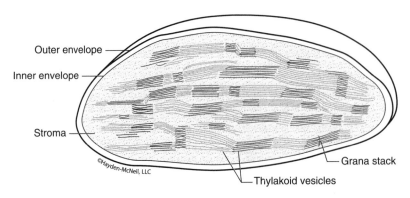

Outer envelope

Inner envelope

Stroma

©Hayden-McNeil, LLC

Grana stack

Thylakoid vesicles

Figure 11.1. Structure of a Chloroplast

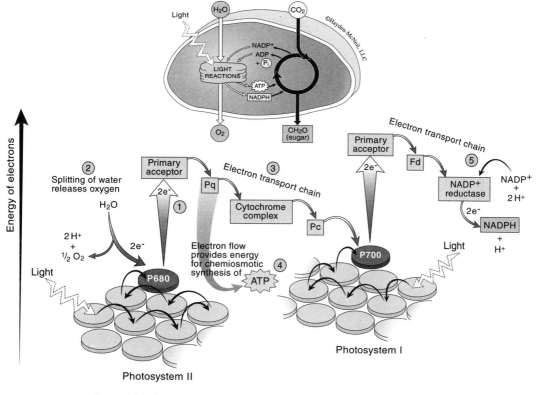

Figure 11.2. Summary of the Light-Dependent Reactions in Photosynthesis

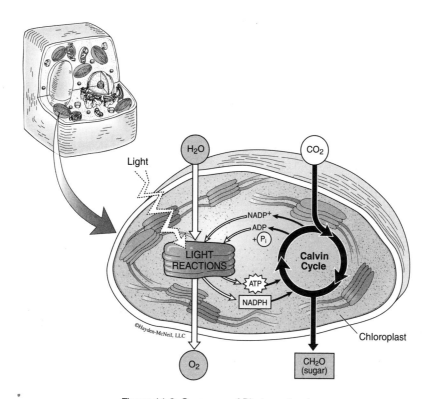

Figure 11.3. Summary of Photosynthesis

Leaves—Structure and Function

Leaves are the primary photosynthetic organs of plants. They are broad, flat organs specialized for collecting light energy necessary for the light-dependent reactions of photosynthesis. Additionally, they contain the entryways to allow the passage of carbon dioxide into the leaf.

A leaf consists of a flat **blade**, and a stalk, or **petiole**, which attaches the leaf to the stem (Figure 11.4). At the point where the petiole meets the stem, there will be an axial bud. This is a dormant apical meristem which, if activated, can form a branch. In dicots, a leaf is defined as the structure that subtends (is found beneath) the axial bud. Some leaves only have one blade—these are known as **simple leaves**. Some leaves, however, consist of several blades all attached to a single petiole. These are known as **compound leaves** (Figure 11.5). There are two types of compound leaves, pinnately compound leaves and palmately compound leaves. **Pinnate** refers to branching or leaflets stemming from a common axis. In pinnately compound leaves, several leaflets originate from the petiole as it extends. **Palmate** refers to branching or leaflets originating from a common point, like the fingers that originate from the palm

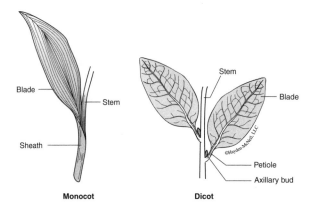

Figure 11.4. Leaf Morphology in Monocots and Dicots

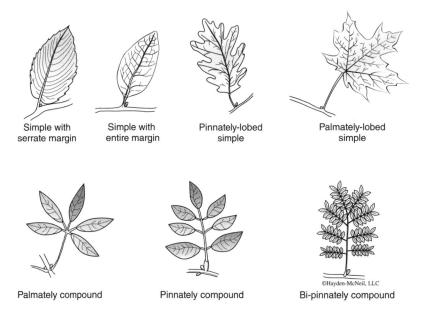

Figure 11.5. Simple and Compound Leaves

of your hand. In palmately compound leaves, all leaflets originate from the end of the petiole.

The vascular tissue of leaves is readily visible as veins. There are three patterns of veins seen in angiosperm leaves: **parallel venation, pinnate venation**, and **palmate venation** (Figure 11.4). Parallel venation has all of the veins roughly the same size and running parallel to each other. Leaves with parallel venation are typically monocots. The other two venation patterns, pinnate and palmate, are primarily found in dicots. Pinnate venation has the secondary veins branching from a large central midvein. The secondary veins branch further, forming tertiary and quaternary veins. The quaternary veins often connect to one another, forming a net-like pattern. Palmate veins, as you may have guessed, have several large primary veins originating from a central point. From the primary veins, secondaries, tertiaries, and quaternaries branch and rejoin as in the pinnately veined leaves.

Two Groups of Flowering Plants— Monocots and Dicots

Within the flowering plants (Angiosperms—see Chapter 13 for more details on this group), there are two main groups of plants: monocotyledons (monocots) and dicotyledons (dicots). The differences between these two groups is summarized in Table 11.1.

In this laboratory, we will be comparing and contrasting the leaf anatomy of monocots and dicots.

MONOCOT AND DICOT LEAF INTERNAL ANATOMY

Obtain a slide showing the cross section of a dicot leaf and observe under the scanning objective. Notice in the middle the pronounced mid-vein. The secondary and tertiary veins will be harder to see because they may be in cross- or tangential-section. Notice how there is a distinct epidermis on the top and bottom of the leaf. The outer surface should have a visible thick layer of wax. This is the **cuticle**. Cuticle wax, a hydrophobic substance, helps to prevent water loss. Leaves have a high surface area, which facilitates light capture but also promotes water loss. By coating the leaves with a layer of wax, water loss through the leaves is dramatically reduced.

One drawback to the waxy cuticle is that it also prevents gas exchange. Plants need CO_2 for photosynthesis, so there needs to be a means to get CO_2 into the leaves. Look on the bottom surface of the leaves. You should see a series of small holes surrounded by two cells with thicker walls. The holes are **stomata** (singular = stoma), which serves as entry points for gasses, and the cells surrounding the stomates are called **guard cells**. Guard cells can open and close, adjusting the size of the stoma.

Inside the dicot leaf you should see two distinct layers of cells. The top layer is the densely-packed **palisade mesophyll** and the bottom layer is a loose arrangement of cells known as the **spongy mesophyll** (Figure 11.6). Cells of the palisade mesophyll have a high density of chloroplasts and are more involved in the light-dependent reactions of photosynthesis.

135

Table 11.1. A Comparison between Monocotyledons and Dicotyledons

	Monocots	Dicots
Floral Arrangement	Parts in 3s	Parts in 4s or 5s
Leaf Venation	Parallel Venation	Pinnate or Palmate Venation
Vascular Bundle Arrangement	Scattered Vascular Bundles	Vascular Bundles in a Ring
Habit	Herbaceous	Herbaceous or Woody
Roots	Fibrous Root System	Taproot System
Growth	Primary Growth Only	Primary and Secondary Growth
Examples:	Grass, Lily, Palm, Orchid	Oak, Roses, Sunflowers

The loosely packed spongy mesophyll are more involved in gas exchange. The air spaces and high surface area of the spongy mesophyll allow CO_2 from the atmosphere to be absorbed into the cells. Why do you think the stomata are typically located on the undersides of leaves?

Now look at a monocot leaf cross section. Notice how the vascular bundles are all about the same size and evenly spaced throughout the leaf. This is because monocot leaves have parallel venation. Also note the tightly packed **bundle sheath** cells that surround the vascular bundle. In many monocots, the Calvin Cycle occurs in the bundle sheath cells. Does the monocot leaf contain well-defined palisade and spongy mesophyll layers?

Absorption Spectrum of Chlorophyll

In this portion of the experiment, you will study the absorption properties of a chlorophyll extract. Your instructor has previously prepared an extract of the chlorophyll from spinach leaves. Since chlorophyll is hydrophobic, this extract was prepared using petroleum ether.

EXPERIMENTAL PROCEDURE

You should obtain two samples, one containing spinach leaf chlorophyl extract and another containing pure petroleum ether, which will serve as your blank. Set your spectrophotometer to 400 nm and then blank the spectrophotometer. Take a measurement of the chlorophyll sample and record the absorbance in Data Table 11.1. Repeat the above procedure for every wavelength indicated on Data Table 11.1, making sure you reblank the spectrophotometer at each wavelength of light.

DATA ANALYSIS

Plot your data on a graph (see Appendix A for graphing instructions). How many peaks does this absorption spectrum contain? Would you predict that photosynthesis would be greatest or least if the plant was given these wavelengths? How does the color of an angiosperm leaf relate to the absorption spectrum you have generated?

Data Table 11.1. Determination of the Absorption Spectrum in Spinach Chlorophyll Extract

Wavength (nm)	Light Color	Absorbance
400		2.374
420	Violet	1.724
440		.510
460	Indigo	.167
480		.143
500	Blue	.248
520		.151
540	Green	.133
560		.046
580	Yellow	.054
600		.127
620	Orange	.151
640		.135
660	Red	.642
680		.424

Light Intensity and Photosynthetic Oxygen Production

The intensity of light is defined as the amount of light hitting a given area over a given period of time. The unit of measurement plant physiologists have adopted for photosynthetic light intensity measurement is:

$$\frac{\mu mol}{m^2 \cdot s}$$ micromoles of photons per square meter per second

The average light intensity outside can range from 100–200 $\mu mol\ m^{-2}\ s^{-1}$ on a cloudy day to over 2000 $\mu mol\ m^{-2}\ s^{-1}$ on a sunny day. In this experiment, you will test the hypothesis that as the intensity of light increases, the photosynthetic rate will also increase. Why do you think this hypothesis is logical?

When the plant absorbs light in the light-dependent reaction, oxygen is produced. Some of this oxygen is used by the plant for respiration in the mitochondria

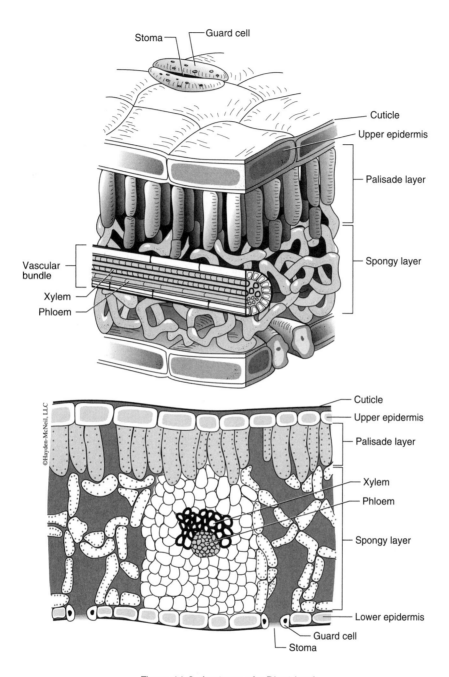

Figure 11.6. Anatomy of a Dicot Leaf

while the rest of it is released by the plant through its stomata. The light intensity at which the rate of oxygen consumption by the mitochondria equals the rate of oxygen production by photosynthesis is known as the **light compensation point**. In this experiment, you will determine the light compensation point for the aquatic plant, *Elodea*.

PROCEDURE

Obtain a piece of healthy *Elodea* about 12–15 cm long. Choose a piece that is bright green—olive green or brown leaves indicate that the plant is not healthy. Obtain a test tube, insert the plant into the tube, and then fill it to the brim with 0.1 M NaHCO$_3$ solution. *Elodea* is an aquatic plant and must fulfil its carbon needs through absorbing CO$_2$ dissolved in water. The two limiting factors for photosynthesis are light and CO$_2$, and since this experiment is looking at the effects of limiting light on photosynthesis, we want to ensure that the plant's carbon needs are met. To do so, we immerse the plant in NaHCO$_3$ solution that contains all the dissolved carbon the plant will need. Therefore, light levels will be the limiting factor of photosynthesis in this experiment.

Obtain the rubber stopper apparatus. Fill a beaker with NaHCO$_3$ solution. Insert the rubber stopper so that the syringe tip is immersed in the solution, and fill the syringe with NaHCO$_3$. Do NOT remove the syringe from the rubber stopper. Carefully place a rubber stopper on the test tube. Try to ensure that there are no large air bubbles between the NaHCO$_3$ solution and the rubber stopper. If there are, remove the stopper, top off the test tube with more NaHCO$_3$ solution, and repeat the above procedure.

Connect a pipette to the rubber hose by the large, flat end (not the pointed end). Now gently push down on the syringe, forcing the NaHCO$_3$ solution into the test tube. You should notice NaHCO$_3$ solution filling the rubber tube and then entering the pipette. Keep gently pushing down on the syringe until the pipette is completely filled with no air bubbles (you may want to place an empty beaker by the pipette tip to catch any spillage). Now carefully

pull back on the syringe until the end of the fluid lines up with the 0.0 mark on the pipette. When you have completed these steps, the apparatus should look like Figure 11.7.

Plug in the fluorescent light and move the ring stand so that the test tube containing the plant is at the lowest light intensity. Wait five minutes to allow the plant to come to equilibrium, readjust the syringe so that the reading is at 0.0 and start taking measurements. As the plant photosynthesizes, any net oxygen production will be released through the stomata. Since oxygen dissolves poorly in water, it will form small bubbles on the underside of the leaves. This will displace the solution, forcing it out of the pipette. The volume of oxygen produced can be measured by watching the bubble end move in the pipette. Record the amount of photosynthetic oxygen production every five minutes for 15 minutes on Data Table 11.2. If the bubble moves in instead of out, that indicates that you do not have a tight seal on your rubber stopper. Stop the experiment and have your TA help you reattach everything.

When complete, move the plant up to the next marked light intensity, allow the plant five minutes to come to equilibrium, readjust the bubble to 0.0 and take measurements every five minutes for 15 minutes. Finally, move the apparatus up so the plant is at the most intense light and repeat the above procedure.

When complete, remove the *Elodea* from the apparatus and place it back where you obtained it. Your TA will give you instructions on what to do with the NaHCO$_3$ solution in the tube.

DATA ANALYSIS

Prepare a graph of the net photosynthetic oxygen production of *Elodea* over time for three light intensities. Generate slopes for each of the best-fit straight lines. The slope is the net photosynthetic oxygen production for that given light intensity. What is the unit of the slope of each line?

Now prepare a second graph with net photosynthetic oxygen production on the y-axis and light

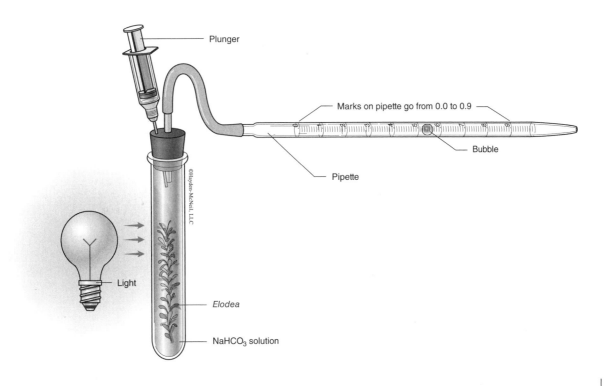

Figure 11.7. Apparatus for the Measurement of Photosynthetic Oxygen Production in Elodea

Data Table 11.2. Net Photosynthetic Oxygen Production of *Elodea* at Three Different Light Intensities

Light Intensity / Time (min)	0	5	10	15	Net photosynthetic oxygen production (ml/min) determined from graph
50 μmol m^{-2}s^{-1}	6	0	0	0	0
100 μmol m^{-2}s^{-1}	0	0.015	0.04	0.085	1.0065
200 μmol m^{-2}s^{-1}	0.085	18 0.09	0.135	0.21	.0191

0   0.09

intensity on the x-axis. You will plot three points, one for each of the light intensity (the x-coordinate is the light intensity and the y-coordinate is the net photosynthetic oxygen production). Draw a best-fit straight line for these three points and determine the equation for the line. Using this equation, determine the x-intercept. This can be easily done

by substituting the value of y = 0 into the equation and solving for x. The value of the x-intercept is the light intensity at which the next oxygen production is zero. In other words, all of the oxygen produced by photosynthesis is being consumed by the mitochondria in respiration. This light intensity is the light compensation point.

PLANT ANATOMY

CHAPTER 12

After completing this laboratory, you should be able to:

- Discuss the similarities and differences between plant roots, shoots, and leaves.

- Compare and contrast monocot and dicot root and shoot anatomy.

- Describe the anatomical differences between an herbaceous dicot and a woody dicot.

- Understand the two types of growth, primary and secondary, found in angiosperms.

- Differentiate between the various tissue types found in angiosperms.

The basic body plan of a plant is much different than an animal. A typical plant can be broken down into two portions, the **roots** and the **shoots**. The roots are usually found underground and have three main functions: they anchor the plant in the soil, they are the primary organ for absorption of water and nutrients, and they are the primary location for the storage of food. Most roots are long and have a narrow diameter, which produces a high surface area to volume ratio. High surface area allows the plant to be efficient at water absorption and to be well-anchored in the soil. The roots grow deep and wide, which further stabilizes the plant. Since absorption is a surface-area phenomena, the greater the surface area of the root system, the more efficient at absorption the roots will be. Additionally, most plants have symbiotic associations with fungi called **mycorrhizal fungi**. Symbotic associations are ones in which both species benefit each other. In this case, the plant benefits because fungi have even a greater surface area than do the plant roots, so they are much more efficient at drawing water, which the roots can access. The fungus benefits because it can access some of the food stored in the roots. A small loss of stored food is a small price to pay for the increased water absorption potential. Food is stored in the roots because most animals have limited ability to steal this food. Being underground protects the stored food.

Shoots are typically the aboveground portion of the plants. There are exceptions to this rule of roots being below ground (prop roots and mangrove roots are above ground) and shoots being above ground (potatoes are shoots below ground), but as a rule of thumb, this distinction holds true. The major functions of the shoots are food production (mostly in the leaves, which are modified shoots), reproduction, and transport of food and water. Several aspects of shoots, such as photosynthesis by leaves and reproduction, will be covered in more detail in other laboratories.

Two Groups of Flowering Plants— Monocots and Dicots

Within the flowering plants (Angiosperms—see Chapter 13 for more details on this group), there are two main groups of plants: **monocotyledons (monocots)** and **dicotyledons (dicots)**. The differences between these two groups is summarized in Table 12.1.

In this laboratory, we will be comparing and contrasting the anatomy of monocots and dicots.

Plant Growth

There are two types of growth seen in plants: **primary growth** and **secondary growth**. Primary growth is growth that results in an increase in length. The tissues responsible for primary growth are known as **apical meristems**. They are usually small balls of cells, or even one single cell, located near the tip of a growing root or shoot. Both monocots and dicots possess apical meristems and exhibit primary growth. Secondary growth results in an increase in girth. The tissues responsible for secondary growth are cylinder-shaped sheaths of cells known as **secondary meristems** or **cambia** (singular = cambium). The **vascular cambium** is one example of a secondary meristem that produces the vascular tissue, xylem and phloem, in plants. Only dicots exhibit secondary growth.

Root Anatomy

In this portion of the laboratory, you will examine cross sections and longitudinal sections of monocot and dicot roots.

Table 12.1. A Comparison between Monocotyledons and Dicotyledons

	Monocots	**Dicots**
Floral Arrangement	Parts in 3s	Parts in 4s or 5s
Leaf Venation	Parallel Venation	Pinnate or Palmate Venation
Vascular Bundle Arrangement	Scattered Vascular Bundles	Vascular Bundles in a Ring
Habit	Herbaceous	Herbaceous or Woody
Roots	Fibrous Root System	Taproot System
Growth	Primary Growth Only	Primary and Secondary Growth
Branching	Rare or absent	Common
Examples:	Grass, Lily, Palm, Orchid	Oak, Roses, Sunflowers

LONGITUDINAL SECTION OF A ROOT

Examine *Slide 1: Radish Root Tip*, under low power (Figure 12.1). Locate the **root cap**, a callous-like covering that encases the growing root tip. It is a rough covering that protects the delicate root tip as it grows through the soil. The cells of the root cap are continually renewed from the apical meristem below it.

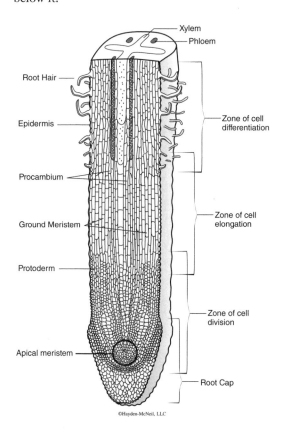

Figure 12.1. Longitudinal Section of a Root

Immediately above the root cap is the **root apical meristem**. The apical meristem is a small region of cells that have remained undifferentiated and maintain a high rate of cell division. The apical meristem of the root is responsible for the primary growth and elongation of the root. The area immediately above the apical meristem is known as the **zone of cell division**. Cells in this zone are still very rapidly dividing by mitosis. After cells are produced from mitosis, they increase in size in the **zone of cell elongation**. Mitosis slows down, but growth along the longitudinal axis increases. This is the area of the root where most of the increase in length takes

place. Further up the root, you will note that cellular differentiation is apparent. This is the **zone of cell differentiation**. It is here that the cells become part of fully functional tissues in the plant.

MONOCOT AND DICOT ROOT CROSS SECTIONS

Examine *Slide 2: Typical Monocot Root* and *Slide 3: Typical Dicot Root*, under low power (Figure 12.2). The **epidermis** is the outermost region of the root. The role of the epidermis is to protect the plant from the environment. Extensions of the epidermis, known as **root hairs**, project outward into the soil and dramatically increase the surface area of the root. Immediately interior to the epidermis is the **cortex**. Nutrients are stored in the cortex, usually as starch grains. The central portion of the root is known as the **stele**. The stele contains the vascular tissue, xylem and phloem, as well as accessory tissues. The **xylem** are the thick-walled cells that transport water up from the roots to the shoots. **Phloem** transports sucrose in the plant. Phloem transport is known as **translocation** and travel is bi-directional. The outer margin of the stele is a thick-walled ring of cells known as the **endodermis**. The endodermis is responsible for regulating the flow of water and dissolved nutrients into the xylem.

Water and dissolved nutrients drawn into the xylem may travel by two pathways, the **apoplast** and the **symplast**. The apoplast is the region between the cell walls of adjacent cells. The symplast is the interconnected cytoplasm between cells. Water enters the symplast by crossing a plasma membrane. However, the majority of water entering the xylem has traveled through the apoplast and has never crossed a plasma membrane. The inherent problem with apoplastic transport is the plant has no means of regulating what enters the xylem. Water contains dissolved nutrients, which are good, but also may contain dissolved toxins or excess nutrients, which the plant does not want to enter the xylem. When water crosses a plasma membrane, the cell can regulate what crosses the membrane and what remains behind. The endodermis contains the **Casparian Strip** on its tangential walls. The Casparian Strip is composed of **suberin**, a waxy substance, which prevents apoplastic travel of water. The only way that

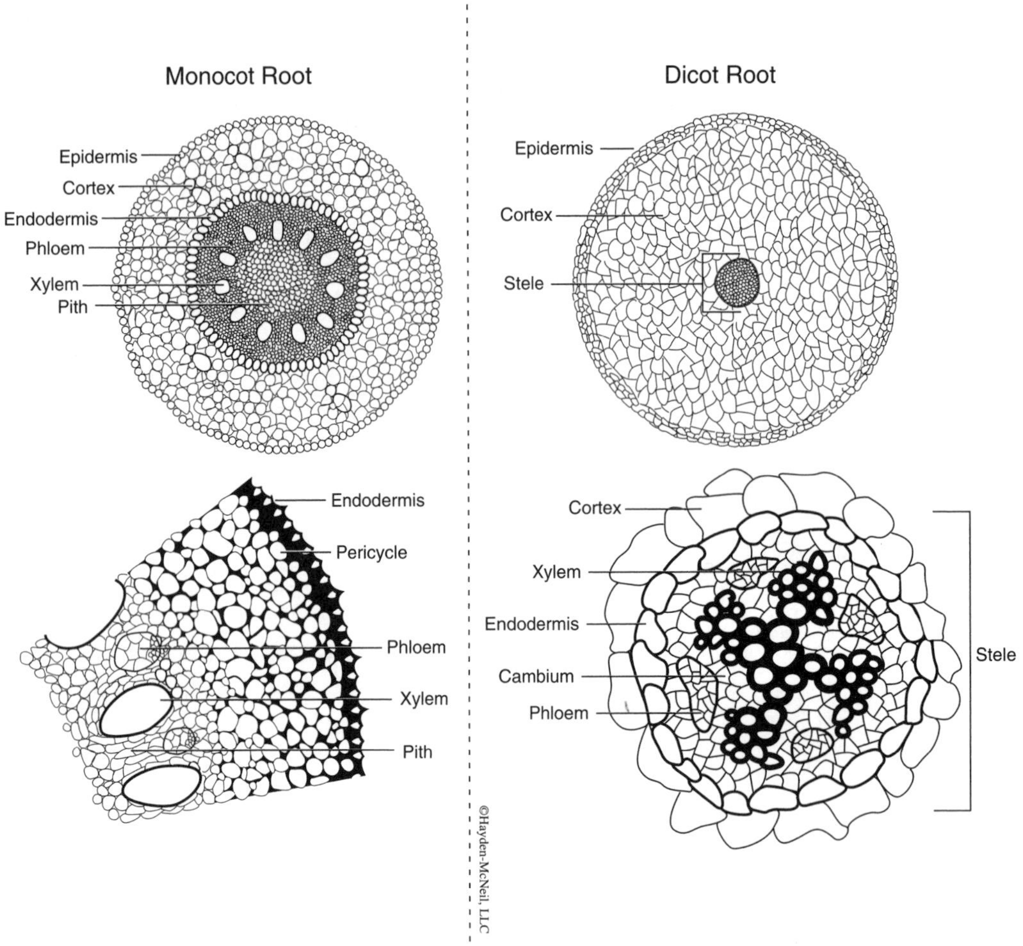

Monocot Root

Epidermis
Cortex
Endodermis
Phloem
Xylem
Pith

Endodermis
Pericycle
Phloem
Xylem
Pith

Dicot Root

Epidermis
Cortex
Stele

Cortex
Xylem
Endodermis
Cambium
Phloem
Stele

Figure 12.2. Comparison between Monocot and Dicot Roots

water can bypass the Casparian Strip is by crossing the plasma membrane of the endodermis and traveling through the cytoplasm. Once past the Casparian Strip, water may remain in the symplast or re-enter the apoplast. However, the plasma membrane of the endodermis has already filtered the water and the water entering the xylem is safer for the plant.

Immediately interior to the endodermis is the **pericycle**. The pericycle is the point of origin of root branches. Since a branch root must be continuous with the xylem and phloem of the main root, a branch must originate from within the stele. The branch root will grow outward, through the cortex, until it bursts through the epidermis. This causes a wound, but this wound is quickly healed. *Slide 4: Lateral Root Origin* will illustrate a branch root forming.

Notice that the vascular tissue in a dicot stem is centrally located—the xylem forms a large, red X and the phloem is in the spaces in between. In a monocot stem, the xylem is located in a large star-shaped ring with phloem interspersed. The central portion of a monocot root is known as the **pith**.

Shoot Anatomy
MONOCOT STEM TIP

Obtain prepared *Slide 5: Coleus Stem Tip longitudinal section*. Like the growing root tip seen in slide 1, a growing shoot tip has a **shoot apical meristem** (Figure 12.3). As the cells mature and elongate, the stem undergoes primary growth. If you examine the cells below the apical meristem, you will see evidence of subsequent differentiations and maturation.

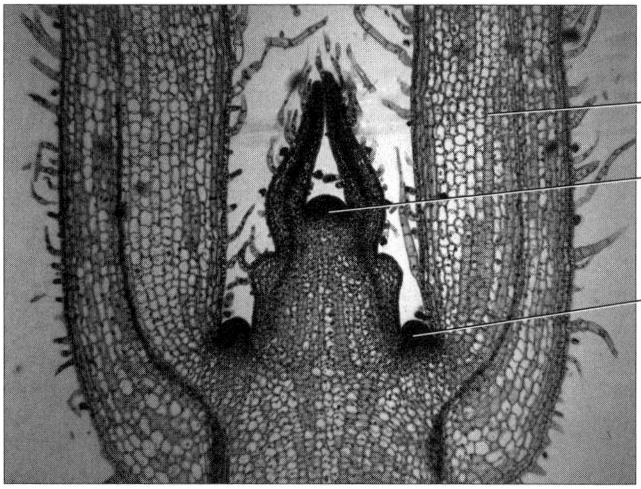

Leaf

Apical
Meristem

Axial "Bud"
Meristem

Figure 12.3. Stem Tip Longitudinal Section

Branching in stems is different from roots. In dicots, branches form from **axillary** or **bud meristems**. As the shoot grows through primary growth, the apical meristem will leave behind bits of dormant meristematic tissue. These become the bud meristems. If you recall from the photosynthesis lab, a leaf was defined as the tissue that subtends the bud. The bud you looked at was the axillary meristem. In the slide, you should see the leaves subtending the axillary meristems. If conditions are amiable for growth in subsequent years, the bud meristem can break dormancy, transform into an active apical meristem, and grow a branch. Monocot stems do not branch and do not produce axillary meristems.

TYPICAL MONOCOT STEM

Obtain prepared *Slide 6: Typical Monocot Stem*, and examine under low power (Figures 12.4 and 12.5). You should immediately see **scattered vascular bundles** distributed throughout the stem (Figure 12.6). The vascular bundle is frequently called a "Monkey Face." The "eyes" of the face are the xylem. The "nose" and "mouth" are air spaces (sometimes there are xylem elements present, too). The "hair" is the phloem. Surrounding the vascular bundle is a ring of **sclerenchyma fibers**. The stem is surrounded by an **epidermis**. Parenchyma cells fill in the stem.

TYPICAL HERBACEOUS DICOT STEM

Dicots are either herbaceous or woody. Herbaceous dicots ("herbs," "annuals," and "biannuals") typically have green stems, show little secondary growth, and die back at the end of the season. Woody dicots ("trees" and "shrubs") have hard, durable stems, much secondary growth, and can live for several seasons. Obtain prepared *Slide 7: Typical Annual Dicot Stem* (Figures 12.4 and 12.5), and observe under low power. You will see an outer epidermis that protects the plant from the environment. Immediately inside of the **epidermis**, you should see several cells with very thick walls. These are **collenchyma** cells. Collenchyma cells are living at functional maturity. The **vascular bundles** are organized in a ring, and aid in supporting the plant, not scattered through the stem as seen in the monocot stem. Running through the middle of the vascular bundles is a ring of meristematic tissue, the **vascular cambium**. The vascular cambium is a secondary meristem that produces xylem to the inside and phloem to the outside. Note that the vascular cambium is continuous throughout the stem. In between the vascular bundles, it is not as active, but will still produce parenchyma cells. Sclerenchyma fibers are associated with the phloem.

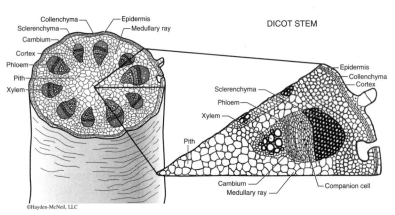

Figure 12.4. Comparison between Monocot and Dicot Shoots

TYPICAL WOODY DICOT STEM

Woody dicots, in contrast to herbaceous dicots, have stems that increase in girth from year to year. Obtain prepared *Slide 8: Basswood Three-Year Stem*, and observe under low power (Figures 12.7 and 12.8). A woody dicot stem can be divided into three regions: **wood**, **vascular cambium**, and **bark**. The wood is the secondary xylem found in the center of the stem. Like all xylem, it functions in water transport and in support of the plant. The vascular cambium is a cylinder-shaped sheath of meristematic cells that produce secondary xylem to the inside and secondary phloem to the outside. Accessory tissues that support the xylem and phloem, like xylem parenchyma, are also produced by the vascular cambium. The bark is divided into an outer region, the **periderm**, and an inner region, the **secondary phloem**. The secondary phloem is layered with many fibers and the overall appearance is cone-shaped. This is due to the fact that the oldest phloem is nearest to the surface. When it was formed, the diameter of the stem was much smaller. As the stem grew in diameter, the phloem became split. The spaces in between the phloem cones were filled in with parenchyma. The periderm is composed of another meristem, the **cork cambium**, and the **cork cells** it produces. Cork cells function as a barrier and protect the plant from pathogens and the elements.

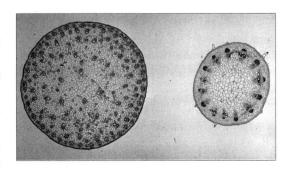

Figure 12.5. Monocot and Herbaceous Dicot Stems

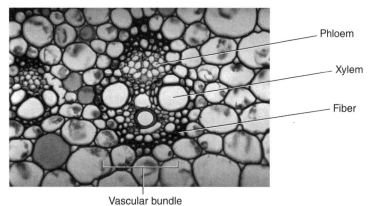

Phloem

Xylem

Fiber

Vascular bundle

Figure 12.6. Monocot Shoot Vascular Bundle
(a "Monkey Face")

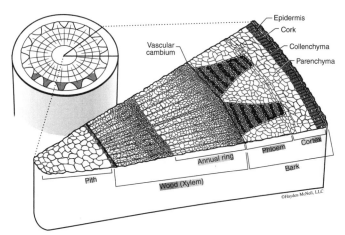

Epidermis

Cork

Vascular cambium

Collenchyma

Parenchyma

Phloem

Cortex

Annual ring

Bark

Pith

Wood (Xylem)

©Hayden-McNeil, LLC

Figure 12.7. Woody Dicot Stem

149

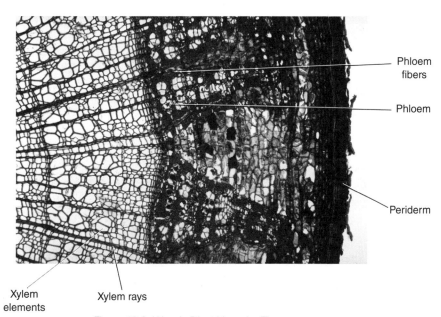

Phloem fibers

Phloem

Periderm

Xylem elements

Xylem rays

Figure 12.8. Woody Dicot Vascular Tissue

As a woody dicot stem grows, more and more xylem elements are produced by the vascular cambium. Conduction of water eventually plugs up the xylem—in actuality, only the outermost three or four layers of xylem are involved in the conduction of water. The rest just serve to support the plant. Xylem formation is in response to the environment. In the spring of temperate regions, rainfall is plentiful. Large-diameter xylem elements are most efficient to transport all of this water. As the seasons progress, water generally becomes less and less plentiful. Xylem elements become smaller and smaller in diameter to better accommodate these drier conditions. In the winter, growth essentially shuts down. The next spring, the cycle repeats itself. This produces a pattern of rings in a woody stem (Figure 12.9). The larger diameter xylem elements are called **spring wood** and are lighter colored. The smaller diameter xylem elements are called **summer wood** and are darker in color. Every year, a new ring is formed. This is why people say you can tell how old a tree is by counting the rings.

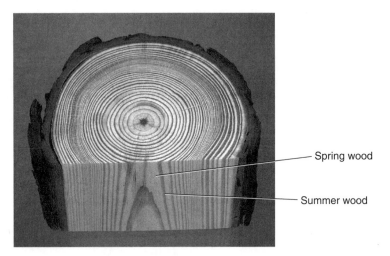

Spring wood

Summer wood

Figure 12.9. Growth Rings in a Woody Dicot Stem

PLANT REPRODUCTION AND DIVERSITY

CHAPTER 13

After completing this laboratory, you should be able to:

- Describe features common to bryophytes, pterido-phytes, gymnosperms, and angiosperms.

- Compare and contrast the reproductive cycles of a moss, a fern, a pine tree, and an angiosperm.

- Discuss the advantages and disadvantages of seed production in plants.

- Identify the major components of a flower and discuss their role in reproduction.

- Identify the botanical origin of foods typically eaten as seeds, fruits, or vegetables.

The Kingdom Plantae is commonly defined as multicellu-lar eukaryotic heterotrophs that utilize **chlorophylls a and b** as their primary photosynthetic pigment. Additionally, members of the Kingdom Plantae store photosynthetic product as **starch** and contain **cellulose** in their cell walls.

Within the Kingdom Plantae, there are several distinct groups such as the bryophytes, ferns, pines, and flowering plants. Most of the distinctions between these groups are based upon changes in the sexual reproduction cycle, so in order to understand plant diversity, one must understand plant sexuality.

Plant sexual reproduction is similar to the reproduction of other eukaryotes in that they utilize sperm and egg. However, what makes plant sexual reproduction special is how the sperm and egg are produced. To better understand this, let's look at a system you are probably more familiar with, animal sexual reproduction.

In animal sexual reproduction, sperm and egg are produced through a process known as **gametogenesis** ("gamete" is a term referring to either sperm or egg—i.e., the reproductive cells). Gametogenesis in animals occurs in special organs known as **gonads**. Gametogenesis in animals occurs directly from meiosis—a diploid progenitor cell undergoes meiosis and produces four haploid gametes.

The gonads that produce egg and sperm are known as the **ovaries** and **testes**, respectively. For sexual reproduction to occur in animals, two organisms come together. If the sexes are separate, these two individuals are the male and female. However, not all animals have separate sexes so we are being purposely vague here. Sperm is released in close proximity to the egg, the sperm swim to the egg, and fertilization can occur once the sperm reaches the egg.

In plants, sperm and egg are not directly made by the diploid plant body. Instead, gametogenesis in plants occurs through a process known as **alternation of generations** (Figure 13.1). In plants, the product of meiosis is not a gamete but a **spore**. A spore is a haploid progenitor cell encased in a thick protective wall. The diploid plant that produces the spore through meiosis is known as the **sporophyte** (spore-producing plant). The organ where sporogenesis occurs is the **sporangium**.

154

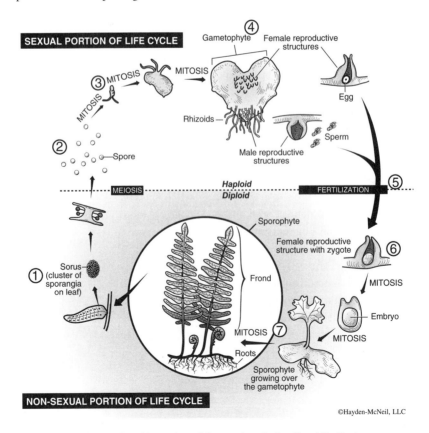

©Hayden-McNeil, LLC

Figure 13.1. Alternation of Generations in the Fern Life Cycle

When the sporangium opens, the haploid spores are released into the environment. They are very small, almost dust-sized, and can travel a great distance if they get a good wind. The spores will eventually land on ground and, if conditions are equitable for growth, the spore will germinate and grow into a small, haploid plant known as the **gametophyte** (gamete-producing plant). The gametophyte is a free-living plant—it is completely independent, capable of producing its own food and obtaining its own water. They are also quite small; a typical gametophyte is no larger than your fingernail. If you have ever walked in the forest in the spring, you have probably walked by thousands of these plants and never noticed them. When conditions are right, gametogenesis will occur in the gametophyte. Sperm are produced in organs known as **antheridia** and eggs are produced in organs known as **archegonia**. Depending on the species of plant, the gametophyte may have separate sexes or they may be hermaphroditic and have both archegonia and antheridia on the same plant.

What must now happen is the sperm must swim to the egg for fertilization to take place. In order for this to occur, there must be a thin film of water present. A light rain or even the morning dew can produce enough water to enable the sperm to swim to the egg. How does the sperm know where to swim? The archegonia release chemicals into the thin film of water. As these chemicals diffuse, a concentration gradient is created. The sperm are positively chemotrophic—they possess structures that can sense these chemicals and they will swim to where the concentration gradient is greatest. Once at the archegonia, they will swim to the egg, fertilizing it.

After fertilization, the resulting diploid **zygote** must immediately grow. Since the zygote is diploid, it is considered sporophyte tissue. Initially, the sporophyte can utilize the food reserves from the gametophyte, but it will soon outgrow these meager reserves and must grow a leaf and start to photosynthesize for itself. If this young sporophyte can establish itself and survive, it will eventually be able to produce spores through meiosis and the entire reproductive cycle will repeat itself.

Plant Diversity

The various plant groups are defined mostly by characteristics relating to their reproductive cycle. We are going to look at four groups and how they have modified this basic reproductive plan. Table 13.1 summarizes many of the characters used to distinguish the many groups of plants.

THE BRYOPHYTES: MOSSES, LIVERWORTS, AND HORNWORTS

The Bryophytes are a group of plants that are commonly called "the amphibians of the plant world." Like their animal counterparts, bryophytes must live near water in order to survive and reproduce. Bryophytes lack vascular tissue (xylem and phloem) and any movement of water or sucrose must be by diffusion. Because this is very slow, most bryophytes are very small to reduce the distance water and nutrients must diffuse.

Table 13.1. Taxonomic Divisions of Plants

Non-Vascular Seedless Plants	*Bryophytes:* Mosses, Liverworts, Hornworts	16,000+ species (most mosses)
Vascular Seedless Plants	Ferns, Club Mosses, Wiskferns, Horsetails	13,000+ species (most ferns)
Vascular Seed Plants	*Gymnosperms:* Pines, Cycads, *Ginkgo*	700 species
	Angiosperms: Monocots and Dicots	235,000+ species

Bryophytes are unique in the plant kingdom in that the dominant stage is the gametophyte stage. When you go out and look at a moss growing on a tree, you are looking at haploid gametophyte tissue. When fertilization occurs, the sporophyte rapidly grows. The sporophyte is typically not free-living—it cannot produce its own food and must be supplied with nutrients by the gametophyte tissue. The sporophyte rapidly grows, meiosis occurs in the sporangia, and the recombinant spores are released. Once this occurs, there is no further need for the sporophyte and it quickly dies (Figure 13.2).

THE VASCULAR PLANTS

All of the plant groups listed below (the pteridophytes and seed plants such as gymnosperms and angiosperms) have vascular tissue (xylem and phloem). They also have the sporophyte as the dominant stage in the life cycle. The gametophyte is either a small, free-living plant or completely dependent upon the sporophyte for survival.

THE PTERIDOPHYTES: FERNS

Ferns are a group of vascular plants that have true free-living sporophytes and gametophytes. The presence of vascular tissue allows ferns to efficiently transport water and nutrients, thus enabling ferns to grow much taller than the mosses.

Ferns have a life cycle exactly as presented in the above description—the sporophyte is the dominant stage, meiosis occurs in sporangia producing haploid spores, the spores are released and grow into free-living haploid gametophytes, the gametophytes produce sperm and egg, the sperm fertilizes the egg, producing a diploid zygote, which grows into an adult sporophyte plant (Figure 13.1).

THE SPERMATOPHYTES: THE SEED PLANTS

There are several disadvantages to the sexual reproductive cycle of the ferns. First, when spores are released, there is no guarantee that they will land in an area where they can grow. If the spores land in

156

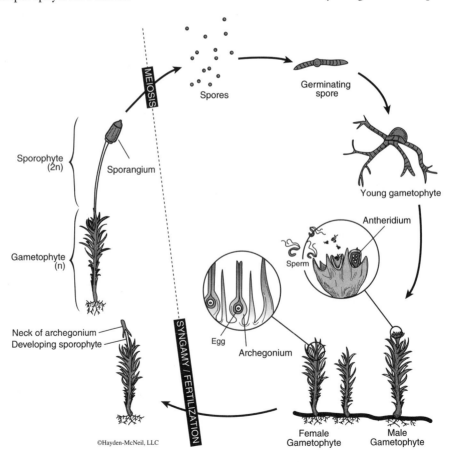

©Hayden-McNeil, LLC

Figure 13.2. The Life Cycle of a Moss

a lake, under a shady tree, or on the sidewalk, they will not be able to germinate. Even if the spore can germinate, the gametophytes are very fragile. If an animal eats it, it will die. If an animal steps on it, it will die. If it is too hot, too cold, too wet, or too dry, it will die. Conditions must be almost perfect for them to survive. Even if conditions are perfect, there must be a nearby gametophyte of the opposite gender for fertilization to take place. If this is lacking, their survival up to this point is meaningless. The life cycle can only be completed if the sperm can fertilize the egg.

The seed plants have circumvented these problems by adopting a life cycle more similar to animals. Instead of producing a free-living gametophyte, the seed plants retain the gametophyte on the sporophyte. By doing this, seed plants can provide the gametophytes with food and protect them from harm. The gametophytes can be raised up high, away from predators, and be provided with all of the food and water obtaining resources available to the sporophyte. One major difficulty with this arrangement, however, is the transfer of sperm to facilitate fertilization. If sperm is produced on the top of a tree, how can it get to the egg in the next tree over? This was solved by a modification of the male gametophyte into a spore-like structure called **pollen**. A typical pollen grain has flat projections that help the pollen glide in the air.

The female gametophyte in a seed plant is protected by the sporophyte within a structure called the **ovule** (note that the female gametophyte is *not* the ovule—it is contained *within* the ovule). Nutrients from the sporophyte are also provided to support the female gametophyte. The ovule itself is usually surrounded by other sporophyte tissue, further protecting the female gametophyte. The egg is produced within the female gametophyte.

When the pollen grain lands on the structure containing the female gametophyte, fertilization can occur. Typically, the pollen grain will grow a tube, aptly called the **pollen tube**, to reach the egg. Fertilization will occur, producing a diploid zygote. The zygote will further develop into the embryo. The

ovule will develop, forming a thick wall. Food will be provided for the developing embryo. The entire ovule will mature and become a **seed**. The seed has three features—a **seed coat**, a **food reserve**, and an **embryo**. The embryo in a seed is dormant. It is living, but all metabolic functions have been slowed down to the minimum required for life. Because the embryo is dormant, it does not need to germinate when it first hits the ground. Unlike a fern embryo that must immediately grow or die, a seed-plant embryo can wait until the environment is most conducive for growth. Embryos within seeds have the ability to sense light, water, and temperature and will only germinate when these and other conditions are just right.

The seed coat protects and insulates the embryo from the environment. The food source will provide nutrition for the embryo once germination occurs. Again, unlike a fern embryo that must start photosynthesis almost immediately, a seed-plant embryo may feed off of the stored food reserves and grow a little taller before forming its first leaf. While producing a seed is much more costly to the sporophyte than producing a spore, the benefits to the embryo far outweigh the costs and have allowed seed plants to become the dominant type of plant on the Earth.

THE GYMNOSPERMS: PLANTS WITH "NAKED" SEEDS

Gymnosperms are the most primitive type of seed plant. When the seeds are formed, they are naked, exposed to the environment. Gymnosperms also produce the food for the seed before fertilization takes place. This ensures that all of the seeds will have adequate food reserves, but can be inefficient as not all of the eggs may be fertilized. The gymnosperm may be producing seeds that contain a food reserve but with no embryo.

Gymnosperms include such plants as the cycads and the conifers. Conifers include the cedars, junipers, spruces, hemlocks, firs, and, of course, the pines. Their life cycle is illustrated in Figure 13.3—The Life Cycle of a Conifer (pine tree).

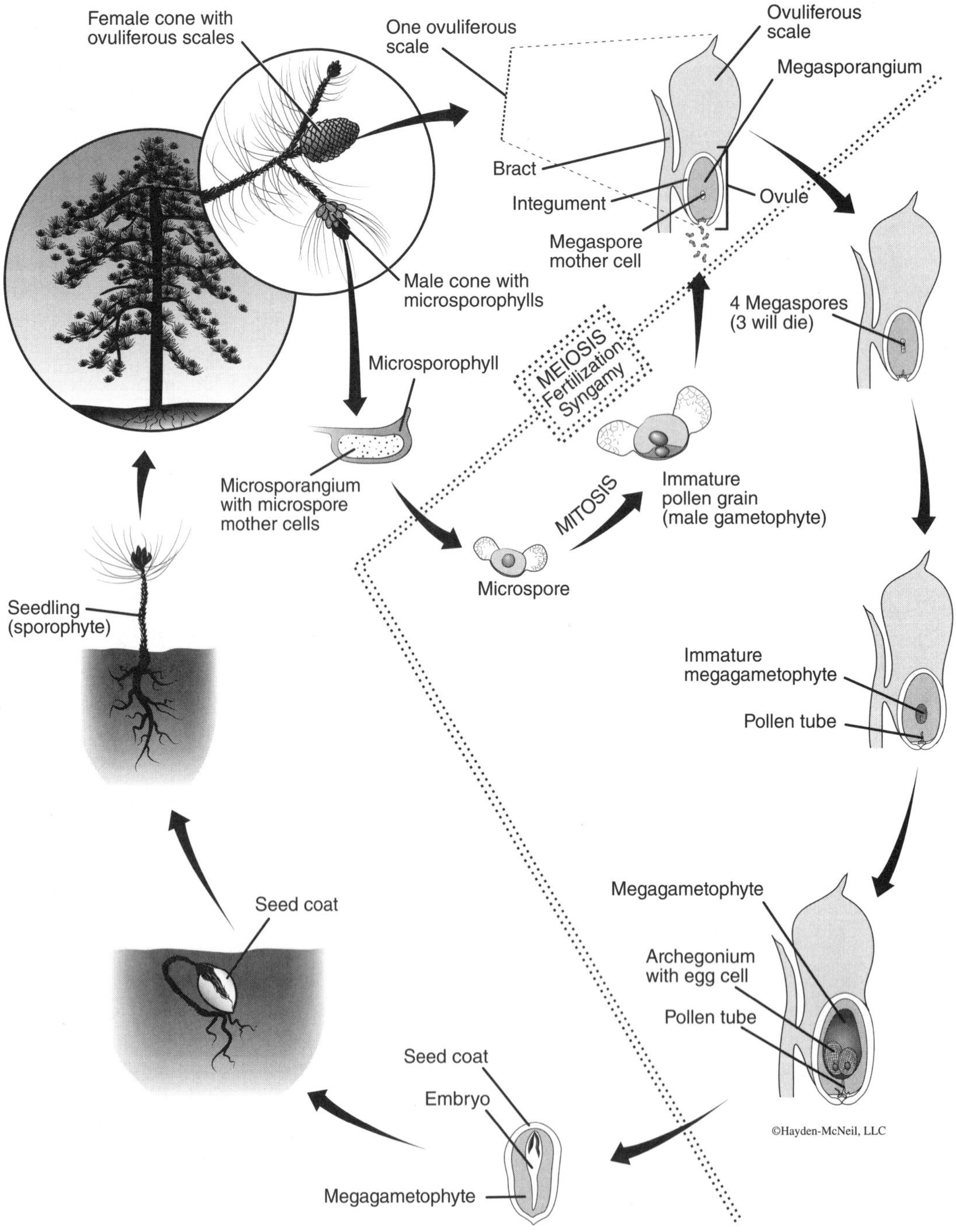

Female cone with ovuliferous scales

One ovuliferous scale

Ovuliferous scale

Megasporangium

Bract

Integument

Ovule

Megaspore mother cell

Male cone with microsporophylls

Microsporophyll

MEIOSIS
Fertilization
Syngamy

4 Megaspores (3 will die)

Microsporangium with microspore mother cells

Immature pollen grain (male gametophyte)

MITOSIS

Microspore

Seedling (sporophyte)

Immature megagametophyte

Pollen tube

Seed coat

Megagametophyte

Archegonium with egg cell

Pollen tube

©Hayden-McNeil, LLC

Seed coat

Embryo

Megagametophyte

Figure 13.3. The Life Cycle of a Conifer

THE ANGIOSPERMS: THE FLOWERING PLANTS

By far, the most diverse group of plants are the flowering plants. Angiosperms have improved upon the basic seed-plant life strategy of the gymnosperms. The two main drawbacks to reproduction of, say, a pine tree, are (1) wind pollination is inaccurate and (2) food reserve production for the seeds before fertilization is inefficient. Angiosperms have improved upon the first drawback by having animals serve as carriers for pollen from reproductive structure to reproductive structure. The second drawback, early food reserve production, has been improved upon by delaying food reserve production until after fertilization. The life cycle of angiosperms is summarized in Figure 13.4.

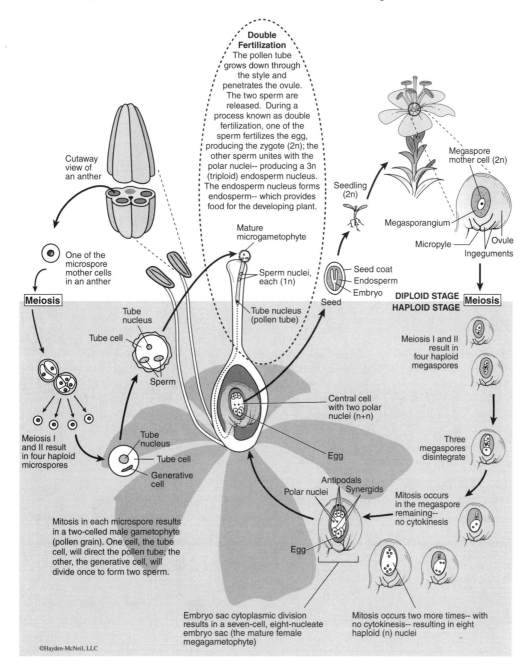

Figure 13.4. The Life Cycle of an Angiosperm

FLOWER STRUCTURE AND FUNCTION

Angiosperms have grouped their male and female reproductive organs together to form **flowers**. Angiosperms have coevolved with animals, typically insects or birds, and utilize these animals as carriers for their pollen. Animals that serve in this capacity are called **pollinators**. Angiosperms provide food for visiting animals. When the animal comes to feed, they inadvertently get pollen stuck on them. The food provided by the plant is not enough to fully feed the animal, so they leave and go to the next flower. The cycle repeats itself, but some times the pollen will fall off the pollinator onto the female portion of the flower, thus allowing the sperm contained within the pollen a chance to fertilize the egg.

A typical dicot flower consists of five components arranged in concentric whorls: sepals, petals, nectaries, stamens, and a pistil (Figure 13.5). The **sepals** are the outermost whorl and they are small, green structures that protect the flower in the bud. The **petals** are the next whorl. They are generally large, colorful, and quite showy. They are used in advertising—the petals are a vibrant display that serves to attract pollinators to visit the flower. The next whorl in are the **nectaries**. The nectaries produce **nectar**, a highly concentrated sucrose solution that serves as the food bribe, which attracts the pollinator.

The male portions of the plant are called **stamens**. A stamen consists of two structures, a long **filament** topped by an **anther**. The filament raises the anther to the appropriate height while the pollen itself is produced within the anther. The female portion of the flower is called the **pistil**. The pistil consists of the **stigma**, the **style**, and the **ovary**. The stigma is a sticky area that serves as the receptive area for pollen on the flower. Pollen must land on the stigma or pollination will not take place. A long style separates the stigma from the ovary. The ovary contains one or more ovules, which, in turn, contain the **egg sac** (also known as the **embryo sac**), which is the female gametophyte. For fertilization to take place, the pollen must land on the stigma and grow a pollen tube down to the ovule. The sperm can then fertilize the egg contained in the egg sac, which is contained in the ovule.

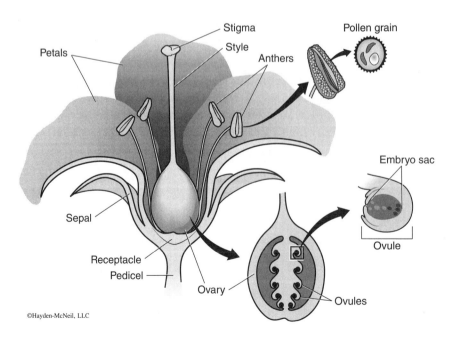

©Hayden-McNeil, LLC

Figure 13.5. Anatomy of a Dicot Flower

THE OVULE AND DOUBLE FERTILIZATION

As previously stated, angiosperms have improved upon gymnosperm reproduction by utilizing animals as vectors to carry pollen from one flower to another. They also have a means to ensure that food for the seed is not produced until the egg is fertilized. This is known as **double fertilization**. To better understand double fertilization, let's take a more detailed look at the ovule and the process of fertilization.

The ovule consists of a **nucellus** surrounded by leaf-like structures called **integuments**. The integuments are sporophyte tissue that completely surround the nucellus except at a narrow gap called the **micropyle**. The micropyle is an opening through which the sperm nuclei will enter in search of the egg (Figure 13.4).

The nucellus contains a **megaspore mother cell**. The megaspore mother cell will undergo meiosis forming four haploid cells. In most plants, three of these cells will die while the fourth will enlarge and grow into a large cell. The nucleus of this cell will divide by mitosis without cytokinesis forming two, then four, and then eight nuclei within the cell. This multinucleate cell is known as the **egg sac**, which is the female gametophyte.

Within the egg sac, one of the nuclei will become the **egg nucleus** and it will migrate to the micropyle end. Accompanying the egg nucleus will be two other nuclei, the **synergids**. The synergids help support the egg nucleus. Two **polar nuclei** will remain in the center of the egg sac while the three remaining **antipodal** nuclei will migrate to the pole opposite of the micropyle known as the chalazal pole.

The pollen grain produces two sperm nuclei. When the pollen tube forms, both sperm nuclei will migrate down the tube. When the pollen tube reaches the micropyle, one sperm nucleus will fertilize the egg, forming the diploid zygote. The second sperm nuclei will fertilize the two polar nuclei, forming a triploid structure called **endosperm**. The fertilization of the polar nuclei serves as a signal for the plant to produce food for the developing seed. These two fertilization events are collectively known as **double fertilization**.

FRUITS

The coevolution of angiosperms and animals for pollination is only the first association that angiosperms have with animals in their reproductive cycle. Angiosperms also utilize their ability to produce food as a reward, and trick animals into dispersing their seeds. After fertilization, the ovary will ripen and become engorged with food. It will typically become colored to better attract animals (where have we seen this strategy before?). A ripened ovary is known as a **fruit** (Figure 13.6). Larger animals such as mammals and birds will be attracted to the fruit and eat it. Often, the seeds are also consumed in the process. The seeds inside the fruit are protected by their durable seed coats and will pass through the animal digestive tract. Eventually, the seed will be passed in the animal's feces, thus dispersing the seed far from the parent plant and depositing it in a nutrient-rich medium.

Not all angiosperm seeds are dispersed this way. Many are dispersed by air or even water. In the laboratory, you will see many examples of animal, air, and water dispersed fruits.

A **vegetable** is an edible plant organ that isn't reproductive tissue. Examples of vegetables are edible roots (such as carrots and beets), stems (potatoes), and leaves (lettuce). You will see examples of many vegetables in the laboratory as well.

162

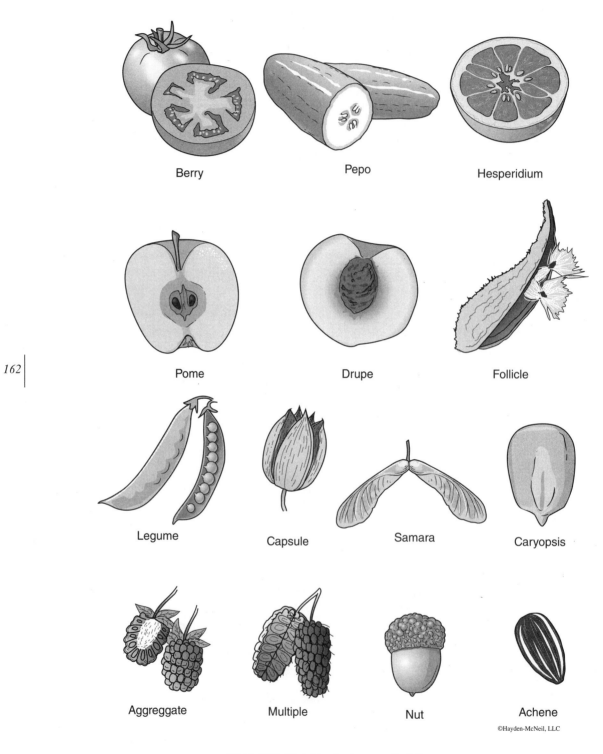

Berry

Pepo

Hesperidium

Pome

Drupe

Follicle

Legume

Capsule

Samara

Caryopsis

Aggreggate

Multiple

Nut

Achene

©Hayden-McNeil, LLC

Figure 13.6. Common Angiosperm Fruit Types

A GUIDE TO MAKING LINE GRAPHS USING MICROSOFT EXCEL™ FOR BIOS 100 USING A PC

A P P E N D I X   A

Part 1: Curves

Just say you've just taken your data for an absorption spectrum and you need to generate the curve. First of all, open MS Excel and enter your data in columns like so (go to http://www.uic.edu/classes/bios/bios100/labs/cheesydataset.xls to download the sample dataset used in this appendix):

Next, put the mouse on cell A1, then click and hold the left mouse key and drag until all of the data set is blocked out like so:

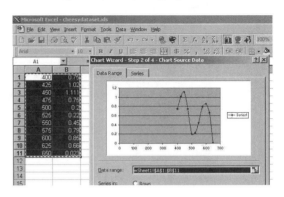

Next, click on the Chart Wizard Button (or click on the Insert menu then select the chart option).

You will then be presented with a series of options.

• First, you must select your graph type. Select XY (Scatter).

• Second, you need to select a type of XY scatter plot. You want to select the option that will create a flowing line graph that still shows the data points.

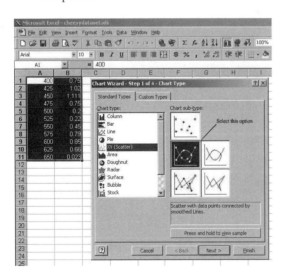

Click on the Next button and you will be presented with a rough sketch of your graph.

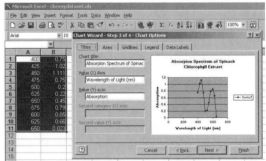

Click on the Next button on the lower right of the box and you will move to another screen.

Enter the title of your graph (Absorption Spectrum of Spinach Chlorophyll Extract) and label the X and Y axes (Wavelength of Light (nm) and Absorption respectively). Then click Next.

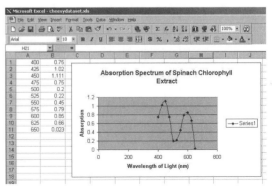

A fourth window will pop up. Just hit the Finish button and the screen should look like this:

This graph is OK, but you can make it better. First of all, the X-axis goes all the way to zero, but the line starts at 400. We can alter the X-axis to start at 375 so that the graph will not be so compressed. To do so, do the following:

* Put the mouse over the X-axis and right click

* A menu should pop up—select Format Axis

* Click on the Scale Tab (the second one)

* Go to the box marked Minimum and change the value from 0 to 375

* Click OK—the graph should change

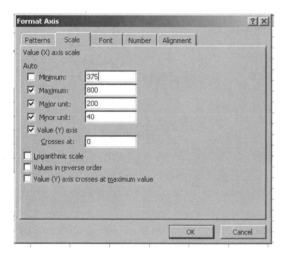

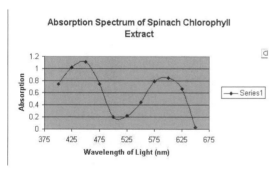

One more thing—click on the box marked "Series" on the graph and hit the delete button (you don't need this label).

Now put the mouse over a white area of the graph, click the left click button so that little boxes appear in the corners. Then select the print button and a full page graph will print out. Easy as pie!

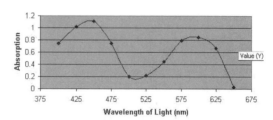

Part 2: Best-Fit Straight Lines

Just say you've just taken your data for an absorption spectrum and you need to generate the curve. First of all, open MS Excel and enter your data in columns like so (you may download the dataset here: http://www.uic.edu/classes/bios/bios100/labs/cheesydataset02.xls). Next, put the mouse on cell A1, then click and hold the left mouse key and drag until all of the data set is blocked out like so:

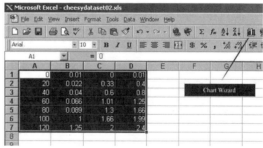

Next, click on the Chart Wizard Button (or click on the Insert menu then select the chart option). You will then be presented with a series of options.

* First, you must select your graph type. Select XY (Scatter).

* Second, you need to select a type of XY scatter plot. You want to select the option in the upper left that is just a series of dots with no line.

- Click Next to move on to the next window.

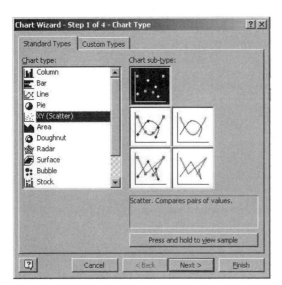

Click on the Next Button and you will be presented with a rough sketch of your graph.

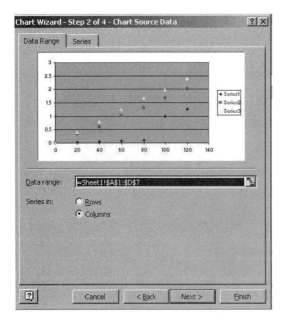

Click Next.

The window will now have selections for graph title and labels for the X and Y axes. Fill these in and click Next.

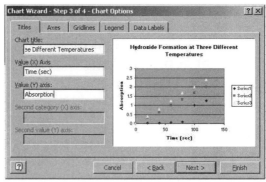

A fourth window will pop up. Just hit the Finish button and the screen should look like this:

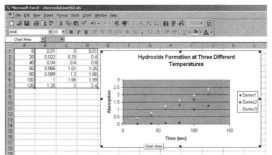

Now, we need to get the best-fit straight line. To do so:

- Place the mouse over a datapoint on one of the lines (in this case, the yellow triangles) and right click. A menu will come up—select Add Trendline.

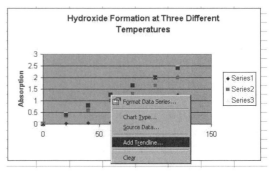

A new window will pop up. Do the following:

- Select the type of line you wish. Since this is a best-fit straight line, select linear.

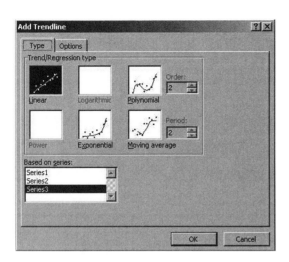

- Click on the Options tab and then select Display Equation on Graph.

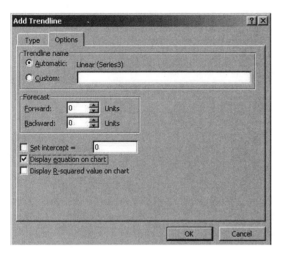

Click OK. Your graph should look like the below left. Repeat the same process for the other datasets. Your graph should look like the one below.

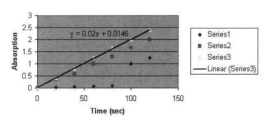

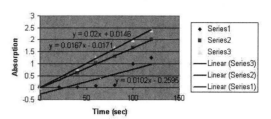

You're almost done. Now all you have to do is label the data points.

Put the mouse over the Linear (Series 3) and left click. The entire legend will be selected. Wait a second and left click again. Now, just the Linear (Series 3) will be selected. Click the Delete key on your keyboard and it will disappear. Do the same for the other Linear sets, so your graph looks like this:

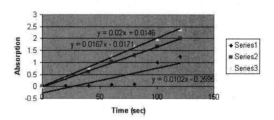

Now, all we have to do is label each series. Put the mouse over a white area on the graph (i.e., an area near the corner where there is nothing), right click and select Source Data. A new window will pop up—select Series1 and type in the data label (in this case, it is 4°C—you can make the degree sign (°) by holding down the Alt key and typing 167 and then letting go of the Alt key. Neat, eh?). Repeat for Series2 and Series3. When you are done, the graph should look like the following page.

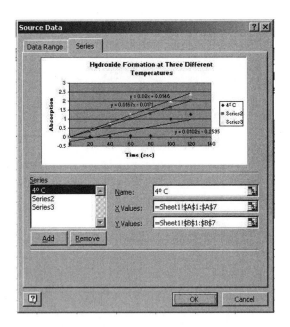

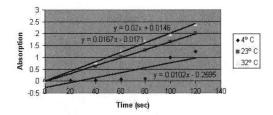

Now you have a graph with three best-fit straight lines and the slope for each clearly labeled on the graph (i.e., in the equation y = 0.02x + 0.0146 the slope is 0.02).

Feel free to ask your TA or Lab Coordinator if you have any questions.